BibleChallenge

Small Facts
from the
Big Book

Daniel E. Harmon

CROSSAMERICA BOOKS
CROSSINGS BOOK CLUB, GARDEN CITY, NEW YORK

Published by CrossAmerica Books, an imprint and trademark pending on behalf of Crossings Book Club, 401 Franklin Avenue, Garden City, New York, 11530

Scripture quotations used in this book are from the Holy Bible, King James Version.

Book design by Grey Thornberry

ISBN: 0-7394-3184-6

Printed in the United States of America

Contents

Introduction

We are delighted to bring you *BibleChallenge*, created exclusively for you, our member. In order to take your Bible study to a deeper, more rewarding level, we set out to design a book that would indeed challenge you—to reach back to Bible stories you may remember and to open your eyes to stories you may find completely new. We want you to have a chance to look more closely at questions that sound familiar but for which you may not have quite the solid answers you thought you did, and to open doors to study the biblical figures and events that intrigue you. Above all, we want to provide a tool that will enrich your understanding of the Bible and assist you on your walk with God. Whether you take the *BibleChallenge* on your own, or with your family and friends, we hope it will remind you of the ageless wisdom of God's Word.

You'll find questions in a variety of styles—multiple choice, fill-in-the-blanks, true or false—on a variety of topics from A to Z (well, *almost*). The quizzes can be taken consecutively, or in any order at all. With the exception of the final quiz, which is comprised of forty questions, each quiz is made up of ten questions. We've put the answers in a separate section in the back so as not to interfere with the flow of the quizzes. We referred to the King James Version of the Bible to compose our *BibleChallenge* questions.

We hope you'll find *BibleChallenge* enlightening, inspiring, *and* entertaining, and that it will bring you countless hours of pleasure and reflection.

Angels

1. An angel appeared to this Old Testament person at Beerlahairoi, or "the well of Him that liveth and seeth me."

    a) Abram
    b) Hagar
    c) Sarai
    d) Jacob

2. True or False: The Bible records no incident of King David encountering an angel.

3. Isaiah refers to Lucifer/Satan, the angel who fell from heaven, as a former _____.

    a) heavenly chariot commander
    b) heavenly gate keeper
    c) prince of wisdom
    d) morning star

4. Which angel interpreted a vision for Daniel?

    a) Michael
    b) Cupid
    c) Gabriel
    d) unnamed

5. At the pool of Bethesda, what did God's angel do at appointed times to bestow healing power?

    a) touched the surface of the pool with a gold rod
    b) disturbed the water
    c) turned the water to blood
    d) made the pool go dry

6. In the parable of the sower and the harvest, which components represent angels of God?

    a) the good seeds
    b) both the good seeds and the tares
    c) the reapers
    d) all the above

7. In Matthew 18, Jesus informs us that certain angels are assigned to look after _____ .

    a) children
    b) old people
    c) animals
    d) gentiles

8. True or False: As Jesus on the Mount of Olives agonized over his coming ordeal, God sent an angel to support Him.

9. Paul told the Corinthians that one day, God's people will be able to _____ angels.

    a) live among
    b) give birth to
    c) judge
    d) destroy

10. We assist "angels unawares," Paul told the Hebrews, when we assist _____ .

    a) our enemies
    b) the poor
    c) strangers
    d) church leaders

Animals
I

1. God substituted this sacrificial animal for Isaac after Abraham passed his test of faith.

    a) goat
    b) ram
    c) calf
    d) pig

2. What kind of animals gave Pharaoh a troubled night's sleep?

    a) lions
    b) swine
    c) snakes
    d) cows

3. When they marched up into the hills, the Israelites were set upon by the Amorites, who chased them like _____.

    a) leopards
    b) horse flies
    c) bees
    d) gazelles

4. Why did Samson torch the tails of 300 foxes?

    a) to destroy the Philistines' crops
    b) to create a smoke screen for his escape from captivity
    c) to flaunt his power
    d) as a sign of God's anger

5. God sent _____ to feed Elijah, who was in hiding east of the Jordan.

    a) doves
    b) sparrows
    c) ravens
    d) crows

6. Because the children of Bethel mocked bald-headed Elisha, they were attacked by _____.

    a) female wolves
    b) female bears
    c) male lions
    d) crows

7. What kind of sea creature swallowed Jonah?

    a) whale
    b) shark
    c) dolphin
    d) great fish

8. The Lord used an angel and a _____ to get the soothsayer Balaam's attention.

    a) donkey
    b) dove
    c) leopard
    d) turtle

9. Jesus overturned the chairs of merchants selling _____
   in the temple.

   a) lambs
   b) doves
   c) goats
   d) rats

10. Revelation predicts an end times plague of _____ that
    will last five months.

    a) ants
    b) locusts
    c) beetles
    d) crabs

Animals
II

1. God describes this animal as having a tail that moves "like a
   cedar."

   a) behemoth
   b) lion
   c) leopard
   d) wolf

2. Which of his sons did Jacob predict would be "a serpent by the
   way, an adder in the path, that biteth the horse heels, so that his
   rider shall fall backward"?

   a) Asher
   b) Dan
   c) Levi
   d) Naphtali

3. Along with manna, God sent this kind of bird to the Israelites in
   the wilderness.

   a) dove
   b) quail
   c) pheasant
   d) duck

4. In Job, the Lord described this animal as stupid—but fast.

    a) hyena
    b) rhinoceros
    c) lynx
    d) ostrich

5. The Lord pointed out to Job that the neck of this animal was "clothed . . . with thunder."

    a) lynx
    b) ostrich
    c) horse
    d) ape

6. Jesus exorcised two devil-possessed men in the region of the Gergesenes at the expense of what kind of animal herd?

    a) oxen
    b) swine
    c) goats
    d) deer

7. Jesus lamented to Jerusalem that He often wanted to gather its children under His care like:

    a) a shepherd gathers lambs
    b) a mother sheep gathers lambs
    c) a hen gathers her chicks
    d) a mother bear gathers her cubs

8. True or False: It was Christ Himself who said that in His name believers would "take up serpents."

9. Jesus empowered His disciples to "tread on serpents and _____."

    a) porcupines
    b) scorpions
    c) black widow spiders
    d) demons

10. Jesus said He would separate the nations at the time of judgment "as a shepherd divideth his sheep from the _____."

    a) wolves
    b) oxen
    c) goats
    d) serpents

Authority

1. This man, both a priest and king, blessed Abram.
   - a) Mamre
   - b) Eshcol
   - c) Aner
   - d) Melchizedek

2. How did David convince King Saul that he had the authority to face the giant Goliath?
   - a) showed him a letter of recommendation from Samuel
   - b) demonstrated his accuracy with the sling in target practice
   - c) told him how the Lord had already delivered David from a bear and lion
   - d) successfully interpreted the king's troubling dream

3. On the shoulder of what earthly man was laid "the key of the house of David," a position central to the king's administration?
   - a) Eliakim
   - b) Eliphaz
   - c) Shebna
   - d) Shimei

4. What authority did the "keys of the kingdom of heaven" bestow upon Peter?
   - a) the authority to act as gate keeper, deciding who would be admitted eternally to paradise and who wouldn't
   - b) the authority to make decisions on earth that would be binding in heaven
   - c) the authority to gain an audience with God on behalf of whomever Peter chose
   - d) not specified in Scripture

5. As reported in the Gospel of Luke, what did Jesus have to say about Caesar's authority?

6. Why did Paul say we must obey human governments?
   - a) because it's akin to honoring our parents
   - b) so the governments will be obligated to shoulder the blame for human foibles on judgment day
   - c) because God, the ultimate power, has ordained these lesser powers
   - d) Paul never taught that we must obey governments

7. What biblical author testifies that the Bible is God's inspired word and "is profitable for doctrine, for reproof, for correction, for instruction in righteousness"?

    a) Luke
    b) John
    c) Peter
    d) Paul

8. Whom did Paul instruct to pray "for kings, and for all that are in authority"?

    a) Peter
    b) Lydia
    c) Timothy
    d) Cornelius

9. Whom did Paul instruct to rebuke wrong-doers "with all authority" and to "let no man despise thee" for doing so?

    a) the church at Jerusalem
    b) the church at Ephesus
    c) Titus
    d) Philemon

10. "Submit yourselves to every ordinance of man for the Lord's sake: whether it be to the king, as supreme; Or unto governors, as unto them that are sent by him" was taught by whom?

    a) Jesus
    b) John
    c) Paul
    d) Peter

Blessings

1. When God promised Abraham a son despite his old age, what did Abraham do?

    a) wept
    b) laughed
    c) raised his arms in thanksgiving and praise
    d) made an offering of a calf

2. As Jacob lay on his deathbed, he bestowed this blessing on his eighth son Asher.

    a) Asher would produce food worthy of royalty
    b) Asher would place his foot on the neck of Pharaoh
    c) Asher would live longer than his brothers
    d) Asher would have more children than his brothers

3. Under Old Testament law, the Lord specifically provided for the poor and strangers by ordering His people:

    a) to store up grain in a specially designated pauper's silo
    b) to take their table scraps to the temple for distribution to the needy
    c) not to be thorough when reaping and gathering in their harvests
    d) not to tithe in the second month of summer, but to give that amount directly to the needy instead

4. Who first delivered to the children of Israel the famous benediction that begins "The Lord bless you and keep you . . ."

    a) Aaron
    b) Judah
    c) Micah
    d) Levi

5. Annoyed at the Israelites' whining about drab food in the wilderness, the Lord over-blessed them, declaring they would get meat "until it come out at your nostrils." What kind of meat did he provide by the ton?

    a) dog
    b) snake
    c) quail
    d) fish

6. Old Testament law taught that among many other blessings, God will "make thee the head, and not the tail" if you:

    a) pray three times a day on your knees
    b) obey His commandments
    c) honor your parents
    d) are among His chosen

7. For his role in vanquishing evil Haman, Mordecai received
   _____.

   a) the king's ring
   b) Haman's estate
   c) neither of the above
   d) both of the above

8. The Holy Ghost promised this man in Jerusalem that he would-
   n't die until he had seen the coming Christ.

   a) Barjesus
   b) Simeon
   c) Zachariah
   d) Trachonitis

9. In the Beatitudes, the first blessed are the _____.

   a) meek
   b) poor
   c) poor in spirit
   d) mournful

10. It's ironic that this, of all places, was blessed by few of Jesus'
    miracles.

    a) Jerusalem
    b) Capernaum
    c) Nazareth
    d) Cana

Books of the Old Testament
I

1. Which Old Testament book provides detailed instructions for
   holy living?

2. Which Old Testament book records Israelite census details?

3. When Jesus stated the underlying law of Moses ("Thou shalt love
   the Lord thy God . . . and thy neighbor . . ."), he was quoting from
   two books of the Old Testament. Which two?

   a) Genesis and Exodus
   b) Numbers and Lamentations
   c) Leviticus and Deuteronomy
   d) Judges and 1 Samuel

4. The Book of Joshua chronicles the Israelites' conquest of
   _____.
   a) Canaan
   b) Egypt
   c) Assyria
   d) Goshen

5. Easily the most famous psalm, it begins: "The Lord is my shepherd . . ." Which psalm is it?

6. How many psalms are in the Book of Psalms?

7. What is the longest psalm?

8. What is the shortest psalm?

9. In essence, Psalm 18 is found where else in the Old Testament?

10. In essence, Psalm 108 is drawn from passages of which previous two Psalms?
    a) 1 and 2
    b) 57 and 60
    c) 90 and 98
    d) 106 and 107

Books of the Old Testament
II

1. The term "scapegoat" ("escape goat") comes from an Old Testament commandment to sacrifice a goat for the removal of sin. Which book describes this?
   a) Leviticus
   b) Numbers
   c) Deuteronomy
   d) Nehemiah

2. Which Old Testament book is largely a love story, exemplifying both romantic love and love and respect for elders?
   a) Exodus
   b) Ruth
   c) Ezekiel
   d) Malachi

3. How many chapters are in Proverbs?

4. The 1960s pop hit "Turn, Turn, Turn" ("For everything . . . there is a season . . .") is based on what book and chapter of the Bible?

5. When we speak of "the handwriting on the wall," which Old Testament book are we recalling?
   a) Genesis
   b) Job
   c) Daniel
   d) Jonah

6. Which prophet wrote Lamentations?

7. Lamentations laments the destruction of _____.
   a) Babel
   b) Babylon
   c) Jericho
   d) Jerusalem

8. What is the shortest book in the Old Testament?
   a) Obadiah
   b) Jonah
   c) Micah
   d) Nahum

9. The prophet Nahum heaped condemnation on what city?
   a) Jerusalem
   b) Jericho
   c) Tyre
   d) Nineveh

10. The Book of Habakkuk:
    a) begins and ends with psalms
    b) begins and ends with complaints
    c) begins with a complaint and ends with a psalm
    d) begins with a condemnation of Israel and ends with a prayer

Books of the Old Testament
III

1. This book records the tragic rebellion of four Israelites named Korah, Dathan, Abiram, and On.

    a) Exodus
    b) Numbers
    c) Joshua
    d) Judges

2. Moses' death is reported in this book.

    a) Exodus
    b) Leviticus
    c) Deuteronomy
    d) Joshua

3. This book tells the story of Othniel.

    a) Exodus
    b) Judges
    c) Ezra
    d) Acts

4. This book tells the story of King David's great-grandparents.

    a) Genesis
    b) Joshua
    c) Ruth
    d) Esther

5. These two books tell the story of King Saul's life.

    a) Judges and 1 Kings
    b) 1 and 2 Samuel
    c) 2 Samuel and 1 Kings
    d) 1 Samuel and 1 Chronicles

6. Included in this book is the story of a godly man named Mordecai.

    a) 2 Kings
    b) 2 Chronicles
    c) Nehemiah
    d) Esther

7. The penultimate chapter of this book records God's description of a leviathan.

    a) Genesis
    b) Leviticus
    c) 1 Chronicles
    d) Job

8. This prophetic book mentions "the circle of the earth."

    a) Isaiah
    b) Ezekiel
    c) Daniel
    d) Micah

9. In alphabetical order, the prophets include Amos, Daniel, Hosea, Joel, Jonah, Micah, and Obadiah (among others). Put these seven books in the order in which they appear in the Old Testament.

10. This prophet spoke at length of a plague of locusts.

    a) Daniel
    b) Hosea
    c) Joel
    d) Amos

Books of the New Testament

1. How does the book of Acts end?

    a) with Peter's death
    b) with Paul's death
    c) with Paul in Rome under house arrest, preaching and teaching
    d) with Nero ordering the destruction of Philippi

2. Put Paul's letters to the Colossians, Ephesians, Galatians, and Philippians in the order in which they appear in the New Testament.

3. In which of Paul's letters do we read of Christ's return?

4. What was physically odd about Paul's letter to the Galatians?

    a) he wrote it on the inside of a cloak
    b) he wrote it in tiny, almost unreadable letters
    c) he wrote part of it in large letters
    d) he wrote part of it with red wine

5. Paul listed the fruits of the Holy Spirit in which epistle?

    a) 2 Corinthians
    b) Galatians
    c) Ephesians
    d) 2 Thessalonians

6. Who, exactly, were the Colossians of Paul's epistle?

    a) the church at Colosse
    b) the church at Colossius
    c) the church at Columbus
    d) the Christian gladiators of the Roman coliseum

7. Paul taught the _____ that if a man doesn't work, he doesn't eat.

    a) Romans
    b) Ephesians
    c) Thessalonians
    d) Hebrews

8. In what letter did Paul state that "the dead in Christ shall rise first" at Jesus' return?

    a) 2 Corinthians
    b) 1 Thessalonians
    c) 2 Timothy
    d) Hebrews

9. The two letters of Timothy were written:

    a) by Timothy to the churches in Antioch and Smyrna
    b) by Timothy to the churches in Antioch and Jerusalem
    c) by Timothy to Paul
    d) by Paul to Timothy

10. True or False: Philemon was a Roman slave.

Christ's Birth and Early Life

1. Christ was born in Bethlehem in the land of _____.

    a) Cana
    b) Galilee
    c) Judaea
    d) Samaria

2. Who was king when Jesus was born?

3. Warned by an angel, Joseph and Mary fled with the child Jesus to _____.
   a) Egypt
   b) Syria
   c) Assyria
   d) Persia

4. God promised an aging man named _____ that he wouldn't die until he saw the coming Christ.
   a) Issachar
   b) Manasseh
   c) Ephraim
   d) Simeon

5. What was the name of the prophetess who recognized the baby Jesus as the Christ?

6. The name Emmanuel means _____.

7. When Jesus was twelve, he got separated from his parents in _____.
   a) Bethlehem
   b) Nazareth
   c) Jerusalem
   d) Jericho

8. Although many people today wonder what Jesus did during his teen years and young adulthood, Luke informs us that he was:
   a) working with Joseph as a carpenter
   b) instructing His immediate family from the book of Isaiah
   c) increasing in wisdom and stature
   d) all of the above

9. After the baptism by John the Baptist, who led Jesus into the wilderness to be tempted?
   a) John the Baptist
   b) Peter
   c) Satan
   d) the Holy Spirit

10. Who ministered to Jesus after his forty days of fasting in the wilderness?

    a) angels
    b) Peter and Andrew
    c) Mary Magdalene
    d) Mary His Mother

Christ's Followers
I

1. Among the disciples who accompanied Jesus, Judas held a special position:

    a) interpreter to Latin-speaking peoples
    b) interpreter to Arabic-speaking peoples
    c) treasurer for the group
    d) scribe for the group

2. What did Peter do that none of the other disciples did?

    a) walked on water
    b) cast out demons
    c) killed a Roman soldier
    d) rose bodily to heaven while still alive

3. Who was the doubting disciple?

4. After Peter denied three times that he knew Jesus, he _____ three times.

    a) pledged his love for Him
    b) dipped bread in the sacred cup
    c) fell prostrate in fear
    d) heard the cock crow

5. When Mary Magdalene brought news that the stone had been rolled away from Jesus' tomb, which two apostles raced to see for themselves?

    a) James and John
    b) Peter and John
    c) Peter and Andrew
    d) Andrew and Philip

6. Who won?

7. _____ was chosen to replace Judas as one of the apostles.

    a) Paul
    b) Barnabas
    c) Matthias
    d) Timothy

8. When Paul was shipwrecked, where was he going?

    a) Egypt
    b) Greece
    c) Italy
    d) Persia

9. True or False: Jesus' brother Joseph was one of the apostles.

10. Revelation was written by which apostle?

    a) Matthew
    b) Mark
    c) Luke
    d) John

Christ's Followers
II

1. Jesus labeled this apostle "an Israelite . . . in whom is no guile."

    a) Andrew
    b) John
    c) Nathanael
    d) Philip

2. Jesus cured one of His disciples' mother-in-law of a fever. Which disciple?

    a) Peter
    b) Andrew
    c) James
    d) John

3. Jesus called Simon, Andrew, James, and John to literally drop what they were doing and follow Him. What common career did they abandon?

    a) carpentry
    b) fishing
    c) herding livestock
    d) tending vineyards

4. Jesus gave James and John, the sons of Zebedee, a surname: Boanerges. What did the name mean?

    a) brothers
    b) fishers of men
    c) sons of thunder
    d) red-faced giants

5. Christ gave the figurative "keys of the kingdom of heaven" to which disciple?

6. Three disciples accompanied Christ to the mountain where He was transfigured: Peter, John, and _____.

    a) Andrew
    b) Bartholomew
    c) Simon the Canaanite or Zealot
    d) James

7. When Jesus appeared among His followers shortly after His resurrection, they were huddled behind locked doors—why?

    a) they feared evil spirits
    b) they feared the Romans
    c) they feared the Jews
    d) all of the above

8. Writing to the Corinthians, Paul enumerated some of the punishments and hazards he had endured during his ministry. Which of the following was not among them?

    a) beatings
    b) shipwrecks
    c) attacks by lions
    d) hunger

9. True or False: Among his many other afflictions, the Apostle Paul is known to have been bitten by a snake.

10. What was at issue in Paul's confrontation with Peter, described in Galatians?

    a) whether Paul should go to Asia Minor
    b) Peter's decision to stop associating with non-Jews
    c) the method of communion
    d) leadership of the early church

Christ's Last Days, Crucifixion, and Resurrection

I

1. When the woman poured perfume on Jesus' head shortly before His arrest and crucifixion, what did Jesus say was the reason?

    a) to identify Him to His enemies
    b) to show her respect
    c) to counteract body odor
    d) to prepare Him for burial

2. On the Mount of Olives before his arrest, Jesus prayed so fervently that:

    a) the ground shuddered, waking the disciples nearby
    b) He sweated blood
    c) He fainted
    d) a lightning bolt destroyed a sycamore tree on the mountaintop

3. With whom did Judas conspire to have Jesus arrested?

    a) two other disciples
    b) Roman army commanders
    c) Jewish leaders
    d) presumably, the criminal underworld of Jerusalem

4. Just before releasing Barabbas instead of Jesus at the demand of the Jerusalem mob, what did Pontius Pilate do to signify he wasn't responsible for Jesus' death?

    a) had Jesus scourged
    b) washed his hands
    c) prayed
    d) fasted twelve hours

5. What was written on the sign Pilate placed on Jesus' cross?

   a) GUILTY UNDER ROMAN LAW
   b) GUILTY UNDER JEWISH LAW
   c) THIS MAN WAS WITHOUT GUILT
   d) JESUS OF NAZARETH THE KING OF THE JEWS

6. Two men were crucified with Jesus. What crime(s) had they committed?

   a) theft
   b) murder and theft
   c) incest and adultery
   d) refusal to pay the Roman tax

7. True or False: Jesus was stabbed with a spear, drawing blood, as He hung on the cross.

8. When Mary Madgalene visited the tomb and first spoke with Jesus, whom did she think He was?

   a) Peter
   b) a Roman guard
   c) a Jewish guard
   d) a caretaker

9. The Roman soldiers who'd guarded Jesus' tomb spread a rumor that Jesus' followers had stolen the body while the guards slept. Why did they lie?

   a) they didn't lie; they believed that was what really happened
   b) Jewish leaders bribed them
   c) they feared they would be severely disciplined or executed
   d) they wanted to debunk the miracle of Christ's resurrection

10. After His resurrection, Jesus ate food with the disciples. What did he eat?

   a) bread and grapes
   b) bread and olives
   c) honey and olives
   d) honey and fish

Christ's Last Days, Crucifixion, and Resurrection
II

1. When Mary wiped Jesus' feet with her hair and perfume, who complained?

   a) Martha
   b) Peter
   c) Judas
   d) Thomas

2. When Jesus rode triumphantly into Jerusalem, adoring crowds lined His path with plant fronds and _____.

3. As Jesus dined at the home of Simon the leper, what specific "wasteful" ointment was poured on His head?

   a) honey
   b) spikenard
   c) myrrh
   d) acacia leaf gum

4. What was the first thing Jesus' arresting officers did when He identified Himself in the garden?

   a) bound Him
   b) dispersed His followers
   c) announced His arrest under Jewish law
   d) fell over backward

5. What did Judas do with the thirty pieces of silver the Jewish priests paid him for betraying Jesus?

   a) gambled it away in a drunken rage
   b) flung it into the temple in a rage
   c) lost it to thieves
   d) bought a plot of land and proclaimed that paupers could be buried there

6. Jesus explained to Pilate that His kingdom was "not of this world." If His kingdom was of this world, He said, His disciples:

   a) would be angels
   b) would be Romans
   c) would fight for Him
   d) would have abandoned Him long before

7. After killing Jesus, the Roman soldiers at the foot of the cross did what?

    a) they spat on Him
    b) they gambled for His clothes
    c) they burned the cross
    d) they drank His blood

8. What did the Roman guards do to the two thieves crucified beside Jesus that they did not do to Jesus Himself?

    a) stole their clothes
    b) gave them water
    c) cut off their thumbs
    d) broke their legs

9. Who joined Joseph of Arimathaea in dressing and burying Jesus' body after his crucifixion?

    a) John
    b) Thomas
    c) Nicodemus
    d) no one; Joseph acted alone

10. When Jesus appeared to His disciples inside the locked room after the crucifixion, what was the first thing He said to them?

Christ's Miracles

1. At what event did Jesus perform his first miracle?

    a) baptism
    b) wedding
    c) Passover meal
    d) funeral

2. Who persuaded Him to perform this first miracle?

3. When Jesus mysteriously eluded the mob of angry Jews in Nazareth, what were they about to do to Him?

    a) hang Him
    b) stone Him
    c) throw Him off a cliff
    d) take Him before the high priest

4. By saying, "Peace, be still," what miracle did Jesus perform?

    a) turning a threatening mob temporarily to stone
    b) calming a storm at sea
    c) causing the sun to stop moving in the sky for three hours
    d) exorcising demons from a child

5. What was the name of the synagogue ruler whose daughter Jesus raised from death?

    a) Jairus
    b) Cornelius
    c) Zacchaeus
    d) Jonas

6. What separate act did Jesus perform while en route to raise the synagogue ruler's daughter from death?

    a) healing Peter's mother from a fever
    b) producing a gold coin for Peter to pay the temple tax
    c) healing the sick woman who touched the hem of His garment
    d) healing ten lepers

7. Which three of the four Gospels record the miracle of Christ walking on a stormy sea?

8. How long had Lazarus been in the tomb when Jesus revived him?

    a) one day
    b) three days
    c) four days
    d) one week

9. Where did Jesus produce a coin for Peter to pay the temple tax?

    a) in a fish's mouth
    b) in a loaf of fresh-baked bread
    c) in Peter's ear
    d) in the tax collector's cloak

10. After His resurrection, Jesus performed what miracle for His disciples at Tiberias?

    a) He fed them with stones turned to bread
    b) He healed Peter's mother-in-law
    c) He told them where to fish
    d) He ascended to heaven

Christ's Travels and Ministry

1. Which four books of the Bible chronicle Jesus' life and ministry?

2. True or False: God sent Jesus to judge the world.

3. When Jesus said one must be born again in order to enter God's kingdom, He was asked, "How can an old person be born again?" Who asked that?
   a) Thomas
   b) Peter
   c) Nicodemus
   d) Zacchaeus

4. On the day Christ gave the twelve apostles some of His miraculous powers, he commanded them to go forth to evangelize and:
   a) defend downtrodden Jews against Roman oppression
   b) heal the sick
   c) baptize
   d) all of the above

5. Foretelling His death long in advance, Jesus told His disciples: "If any man will come after me, let him _____ himself, and take up his _____, and follow me."
   a) humble/bitter drink
   b) deny/cross
   c) scourge/crown of thorns
   d) try/scarlet cloak

6. Why did Zacchaeus invite Jesus to dinner?
   a) Zacchaeus wanted to formally present half his possessions to the poor
   b) to hear Christ teach
   c) to take communion
   d) Zacchaeus didn't invite Jesus to dinner; Jesus invited Himself to Zacchaeus' house

7. Why is the transfiguration called that?
   a) because Jesus changed water into wine
   b) because Jesus and His clothes became radiant
   c) because Jesus made evil spirits enter a herd of swine
   d) because Jesus gave His followers the Holy Spirit

8. With which two Old Testament leaders did Jesus speak at the transfiguration?

9. John 11:35 records: "Jesus wept." Why did He weep?

    a) over the death of His earthly father Joseph
    b) over the death of John the Baptist
    c) over the death of Lazarus
    d) over His own coming ordeal and death

10. Jesus told the scribes and Pharisees they were like "whitewashed _____."

    a) fences
    b) corpses
    c) tombs
    d) none of the above

Cloak and Dagger
I

1. True or False: Genesis 31 tells the story of Laban tricking Jacob and being forced to flee.

2. The Jericho harlot who concealed Joshua's spies was _____.

    a) Rahab
    b) Sylvia
    c) Sylvia's mother
    d) Deborah

3. This left-handed judge delivered the Israelites from bondage under the Moabites by assassinating King Eglon with a knife.

    a) Othniel
    b) Ehud
    c) Caleb
    d) Shamgar

4. What woman was Samson's undoing, revealing to his enemies the source of his great strength?

5. King Saul disguised himself and secretly visited a witch at
   _____.

    a) Philadelphia
    b) Endor
    c) Marada
    d) Zarephath

6. During the bloody upheaval when David succeeded Saul, a man
   named Joab murdered a man named Abner. Who were they?

    a) David and Saul's respective uncles
    b) David and Saul's respective army commanders
    c) David and Saul's respective armor bearers
    d) David and Saul's respective brothers

7. How did Absalom die?

    a) he accidentally caught his head in a tree while riding a
   mule, leaving him hanging
    b) Joab, David's general, pierced his heart with darts
    c) Joab's armor bearers slew him
    d) all of the above

8. True or False: Jeroboam at one point was an outcast living in
   Egypt, hiding from Solomon.

9. What leader vowed to kill Elijah the prophet?

    a) King Benhadad
    b) King Saul
    c) Queen Jezebel
    d) the Queen of Sheba

10. "The fathers shall not be put to death for the children, neither
    shall the children be put to death for the fathers: every man
    shall be put to death for his own sin." This Old Testament law
    (Deuteronomy 24:16) moderated the wrath of what king when he
    avenged the murder of his father?

    a) Amaziah
    b) Jeroboam
    c) Ahaziah
    d) Joah

Cloak and Dagger
II

1. What was the first act of murder recorded in the Bible?

2. Whose birthright was stolen by his mother and brother?

3. Jacob didn't know it, but his wife Rachel stole something from her father Laban, which soon got them into trouble. What did she steal?
   - a) a golden chalice
   - b) a silver chalice
   - c) food
   - d) idols

4. Where did Rachel hide the loot she stole from her father?
   - a) in the servants' tent
   - b) in her sister Leah's tent
   - c) beneath her, packed aboard a camel
   - d) buried beneath stones at Galeed

5. What price did Joseph's brothers receive for selling him to the merchants bound for Egypt?
   - a) ten pieces of silver
   - b) twenty pieces of silver
   - c) thirty pieces of silver
   - d) forty pieces of gold

6. Joseph deliberately got his beloved brother Benjamin into trouble. How?
   - a) by telling Reuben that Benjamin had revealed the older brothers' deceit to their father Jacob
   - b) by telling Pharaoh that Benjamin was a spy
   - c) by giving Benjamin a fortune in gems from the Pharaoh's treasury
   - d) by making it appear Benjamin had stolen Joseph's own silver cup

7. This woman drove a nail into the head of sleeping Sisera, commander of the fearsome Canaanite charioteers.

   a) Deborah
   b) Shua
   c) Jael
   d) Hannah

8. What tricky word did Jephthah and the Gileadites use to expose their enemies from Ephraim who were trying to escape across the River Jordan?

9. Why was the high priest Ahimelech slain?

   a) for defiling the temple
   b) for offering unclean sacrifices
   c) for supporting David against Saul
   d) for supporting Saul against David

10. This evil queen seized power by murdering the royal descendants after her son Ahaziah's death. However, she failed to kill one grandson, Joash, who emerged from protective custody six years later, took the throne, and ordered her execution.

    a) Athaliah
    b) Cleopatra
    c) Jezebel
    d) Keziah

Cloak and Dagger
III

1. Besides Lot and his wife, whom did the angels lead out of Sodom?

2. What did God do to Moses' ten spies who brought back negative reports from Canaan?

   a) commanded Moses to place them in the front line of battle
   b) stripped them of their armor
   c) stripped them of their households
   d) let them die in a plague

3. After leaving his weapons behind as he fled in haste from King Saul, the fugitive David was given a very special weapon by Ahimelech the priest. What was it?

 a) the knife with which Abraham intended to sacrifice Isaac
 b) the rod of Aaron
 c) the sword with which David had killed Goliath
 d) King Saul's ceremonial dagger

4. To whom did Nathan first report Adonijah's plot to seize the throne of Israel?

 a) King David
 b) Solomon
 c) Bathsheba
 d) Benaiah

5. This man grabbed King Benhadad's throne by smothering Benhadad with a wet blanket.

 a) Hazael
 b) Ahaziah
 c) Jehoram
 d) Jehu

6. Jehu slyly killed these two kings and seized power.

 a) Joram and Ahaziah
 b) Benhadad and Jehoram
 c) Amaziah and Jeroboam
 d) Pekah and Ahaz

7. This king was assassinated by his sons Adrammelech and Sharezer—neither of whom succeeded him.

 a) Saul
 b) Solomon
 c) Shalman
 d) Sennacherib

8. Who hid the royal child Joash for six years from execution by his wicked grandmother?

 a) Ahaziah
 b) Jehoshabeath
 c) Jehoram
 d) Jetheth

9. This governor of Judah, appointed by Babylonian King Nebuchadnezzar, was assassinated because of his lenient policy toward Jewish captives.

    a) Jehoiachin
    b) Zedekiah
    c) Gedaliah
    d) Elishama

10. By what device did Paul escape an assassination plot in Damascus?

    a) he exited the city gates disguised with a false beard
    b) he exited the city gates hidden in the baggage of an ox cart
    c) he mysteriously passed through a mob just as Jesus once had done
    d) he was lowered over the side of the city wall in a basket under the cover of darkness

Clothing

1. Whose mother made him kidskin gloves?

    a) Isaac's
    b) Jacob's
    c) Joseph's
    d) Samuel's

2. What did the book of Leviticus have to say about men's beards?

    a) they shouldn't be allowed to grow until a youth reached age twenty
    b) they should be shaved and restarted every seven years
    c) the edges shouldn't be trimmed
    d) they should be trimmed at ten inches

3. What did the Israelites wear in the wilderness?

    a) sackcloth
    b) clothes of animal hides
    c) clothes of wool
    d) the same clothes for forty years

4. When Samuel was a child serving the temple, what did his mother bring him each year?

    a) new shoes
    b) a new coat
    c) a scarlet cap
    d) a silver bracelet

5. Who at one time had their garments cut to the hips?

    a) Delilah
    b) Bathsheba
    c) David's servants
    d) Herodias' daughter

6. What prophet criticized strange apparel?

    a) Jeremiah
    b) Micah
    c) Nahum
    d) Zephaniah

7. Beneath the cross, what feature of Jesus' coat prompted the Roman soldiers to cast lots for it rather than divide it into quarters?

    a) it wouldn't tear because it was made of wool
    b) they considered it a valuable relic
    c) it was seamless
    d) it was intricately embroidered

8. Of what is the clothing worn by the virtuous woman of Proverbs 31 made?

    a) silk
    b) kidskin
    c) sackcloth
    d) twined linen

9. In admonishing women to dress modestly, Paul specifically banned "braided hair, or gold, or _____ , or costly array."

    a) shoes
    b) silver
    c) diamonds
    d) pearls

10. True or False: Paul complimented women with long hair.

Colors

1. What color was Esau at birth?
    a) pale blue
    b) pink
    c) red
    d) yellow

2. In His instructions for furnishing the tabernacle, God told Moses the curtains should be of three specific colors. Name two of them.

3. For the cleansing offering, God told Moses and Aaron to present an unblemished, unworked heifer the color of _____.
    a) white
    b) black
    c) white with black splashes
    d) red

4. In denouncing Samaria as the figurative prostitute Ahola, Ezekiel described her lovers as Assyrian horsemen uniformed in _____.
    a) black
    b) blue
    c) crimson
    d) gold

5. What color was the robe in which the Roman soldiers cloaked Jesus?
    a) white
    b) black
    c) scarlet/purple
    d) green

6. The angel who rolled back the stone from Jesus' tomb was clothed in _____.
    a) white
    b) black
    c) scarlet/purple
    d) green

7. What color is the rainbow surrounding the throne in heaven, as described by John in Revelation?

    a) ochre
    b) emerald
    c) rose
    d) multicolored

8. Seated around the throne, as described in Revelation, are twenty-four elders dressed in what color?

    a) white
    b) black
    c) blood red
    d) sky blue

9. Of the four horsemen of the apocalypse described by John in Revelation, which horse appears first?

    a) black
    b) white
    c) brown
    d) red

10. Among the four horsemen of the apocalypse, what is the name of the rider of the pale horse?

Conversions

1. In the end, King Nebuchadnezzar ruled in a godly manner. First, however, God cast him into the wilderness where:

    a) he worshipped Baal
    b) he was without food for forty days
    c) he had a near-death experience
    d) his nails grew long as bird claws

2. True or False: Jesus Himself never used the term "born again" in revealing how to obtain salvation.

3. After Peter's message at the Pentecost, how many were baptized?

    a) 24
    b) 240
    c) 300
    d) 3,000

4. When Saul/Paul converted, who baptized him?

   a) Peter
   b) John
   c) Ananias
   d) Barnabas

5. Paul blinded the false prophet Barjesus for a season and thereby converted what government official?

   a) Cornelius
   b) Barnabas
   c) Cis
   d) Sergius Paulus

6. Lydia's conversion and baptism took place in _____ .

   a) Syria
   b) Pamphylia
   c) Macedonia
   d) Sicily

7. What event prompted the jailer at Philippi to convert to Christianity?

   a) the death of his son
   b) the healing of his son
   c) an earthquake that decimated his prison and thus could have brought about his downfall
   d) the appearance of a blinding light and a voice speaking from it

8. Dionysius and Damaris were converted to Christianity at _____ .

   a) Athens
   b) Philadelphia
   c) Rome
   d) Ephesus

9. As proof of their conversion at Ephesus, described in Acts, what did the magicians do?

   a) tore their clothes
   b) burned their magic books
   c) fell on their faces three times
   d) spoke in tongues

10. In his epistles, Paul commended these believers for the way they had "turned to God from idols to serve the living and true God."

  a) Romans
  b) Colossians
  c) Thessalonians
  d) Hebrews

Creation

1. What were the first two things God created?

  a) earth and sea
  b) earth and sky
  c) earth and wind
  d) wind and water

2. What was God's first recorded statement?

  a) "It is good."
  b) "It is not good."
  c) "Let there be light."
  d) "This is the day that I have made."

3. On which day did God create the land and vegetation?

  a) third
  b) fourth
  c) fifth
  d) sixth

4. God created celestial lights dividing night from day in order to show four specific things: days, seasons, years, and _____.

  a) human generations
  b) centuries
  c) millennia
  d) none of the above

5. On which day did God create man?

  a) first
  b) second
  c) sixth
  d) seventh

6. God created man on the same day He created _____ .

    a) the firmament
    b) the sea and sky creatures
    c) the land creatures
    d) the sea, sky, and land creatures

7. True or False: God made man in the image of His cherubim.

8. According to the writer of Genesis, when God looked on His new creation, what was His assessment?

9. What was God's first command to humans?

    a) to clothe themselves with fig leaves
    b) to bow down and worship Him
    c) to have children
    d) to take charge of all wildlife

10. How did God water the earth after completing the creation?

    a) with a spring of water from Goshen
    b) with a pervasive mist
    c) with three days and nights of rain
    d) with the great flood

Crime and Punishment
I

1. The Old Testament prescribed as punishment "eye for eye," "tooth for tooth". . . and among other things, what else?

    a) "stab for stab"
    b) "stripe for stripe"
    c) "head for head"
    d) "ear for ear"

2. According to Old Testament law, if you were caught stealing an ox, what was the punishment?

    a) repaying with two oxen
    b) repaying with five oxen
    c) having one of your thumbs severed
    d) death

3. According to Old Testament law, if two people contested owner-ship of property, the one who lost the case before the judges must:

   a) pay double the worth of the property to the other
   b) go into exile for one year
   c) be cast into a dungeon for one year
   d) work for the other for one year

4. According to Old Testament law, what was the punishment for hitting your father or mother?

   a) banishment from the tribe with no inheritance
   b) cutting off the right hand
   c) death
   d) the Bible records no punishment for such an offense

5. According to Old Testament law, what was the punishment for cursing your father or mother?

   a) banishment from the tribe with no inheritance
   b) cutting off the right hand
   c) death
   d) the Bible records no punishment for such an offense

6. True or False: The law of Moses required capital punishment for murder even if the murderer came before God's altar.

7. True or False: The law of Moses was lenient toward the killer in cases of accidental death, allowing the killer to flee for his life.

8. According to Old Testament law, what was the punishment for kidnapping?

   a) one year's servitude to the victim or, if a child, to the victim's family
   b) lifelong servitude to the victim or, if a child, to the victim's family
   c) death
   d) the Bible records no punishment for such an offense

9. According to Old Testament law, if a man injured another in a fight, the punishment was _____.

   a) compensation for any losses and support of the victim during convalescence
   b) a fine of forty gold pieces
   c) death
   d) nothing, unless the victim died

10. According to Old Testament law, if your ox fatally gored someone:

   a) you must support the victim's family for one generation
   b) if the ox had a prior record of meanness, both you and your ox must be put to death, unless the victim's family agreed to accept restitution; if it was the ox's first offense, your ox must be slaughtered but you would not face personal punishment
   c) if the ox had a prior record, both you and your ox would be executed with no hope of reprieve; if it was the ox's first offense, your ox must be hobbled permanently but you faced no personal punishment
   d) the Bible records no punishment for such an offense

Crime and Punishment
II

1. When Moses saw an Egyptian slave master beating a Hebrew worker, he delivered this punishment to the Egyptian.

   a) he reported him to Pharaoh
   b) he beat the Egyptian within an inch of his life
   c) he slew the Egyptian
   d) he slew the Egyptian's family

2. The first reported incident of capital punishment by stoning occurred while the Israelites wandered in the wilderness. What was the offense?

   a) theft of an ox
   b) adultery
   c) Sabbath breaking
   d) beating a parent

3. According to Old Testament law, the punishment for witchcraft was _____.

   a) loss of both eyes
   b) loss of the right eye
   c) banishment
   d) death

4. According to Old Testament law, the punishment for making a sacrifice to a false god was _____.

    a) utter destruction
    b) death by fire
    c) death by the sword
    d) death by hanging

5. In what book of the Bible does God authorize havens of rest for those who commit manslaughter?

    a) Genesis
    b) Numbers
    c) Psalms
    d) Matthew

6. What punishment did Joshua prescribe for the five Amorite kings who rose against him?

    a) banishment
    b) lifelong confinement within their palaces
    c) execution
    d) none—they all were killed in battle

7. Some of the men of this city were killed because they looked inside the Ark of the Covenant.

    a) Dibon
    b) Heshbon
    c) Ziklag
    d) Bethshemesh

8. King Solomon ordered the execution of this old enemy of his father David for violating a detention order.

    a) Jehoiada
    b) Benaiah
    c) Shimei
    d) Sibbechai

9. True or False: Proverbs says a man is not despised if he steals out of hunger.

10. Who taught that before you take formal action against someone who sins against you, you must "go and tell him his fault between thee and him alone"?

    a) God through Moses
    b) Jesus
    c) Solomon
    d) Paul

Curses and Condemnations

1. Who did God condemn to eat dust the rest of his life?

   a) Adam
   b) Cain
   c) Lot
   d) the serpent

2. Reuben took his father Jacob's concubine for himself. What did this cost him?

   a) a curse of impotence
   b) the birth of a wayward son
   c) loss of his preeminence as oldest son
   d) loss of his life

3. While blessing most of their brothers, Jacob cursed Simeon and Levi and foretold the scattering of their descendants. Why?

   a) their disrespect for him
   b) their anger and cruelty
   c) their sexual sins
   d) their treatment of Joseph

4. True or False: Old Testament law placed a curse on anyone who moved a neighbor's property markers.

5. Who proclaimed a curse against any man who rebuilt the city of Jericho?

   a) Joshua
   b) Elijah
   c) Solomon
   d) God

6. For embezzlement, Elisha cursed his servant Gehazi, as well as Gehazi's descendants, with _____.

   a) baldness
   b) leprosy
   c) weak hearts
   d) lives of tilling the earth for cruel masters

7. In Isaiah, the Lord vowed that the wicked:

   a) would be doomed to unquenchable thirst
   b) would serve the just
   c) would serve the poor
   d) would have no peace

8. Because of this prophet's wayward teaching, God through Jeremiah condemned him to a quick death.

   a) Hananiah
   b) Jedaiah
   c) Noadiah
   d) Tobiah

9. What city did Jesus say would face worse punishment than Sodom because it ignored His mighty works there?

   a) Bethlehem
   b) Nazareth
   c) Bethsaida
   d) Capernaum

10. Jesus cursed what kind of tree?

   a) palm
   b) sycamore
   c) fig
   d) He didn't curse a tree; He cursed some of a tree's fruit

Death

1. What did God warn Adam would cause certain death?

2. Whose was the first human death recorded in the Bible?

   a) Adam's
   b) Eve's
   c) Abel's
   d) Methuselah's

3. How did Rachel die?

   a) killed in a raid by the Perizzites
   b) giving birth
   c) of leprosy
   d) apparently of old age

4. What stingy livestock owner in King David's time died of an apparent stroke or heart attack after lingering ten days "as a stone"?

    a) Abiathar
    b) Nabal
    c) Ahio
    d) Obededom

5. What royal person died by being thrown into the streets by servants and trampled by horses?

    a) King Saul
    b) Prince Adonijah
    c) Queen Vashti
    d) Queen Jezebel

6. "What man is he that liveth, and shall not see death? Shall he deliver his soul from the hand of the grave?" Who uttered that lament?

    a) Elijah
    b) Job
    c) one of the psalmists
    d) Paul

7. Whose death made it possible for Joseph and Mary to return from exile in Egypt with Jesus?

8. Whose death prompted many graves to open and long-dead saints to appear bodily throughout Jerusalem?

    a) Jesus'
    b) David's
    c) John the Baptist's
    d) Stephen's

9. True or False: Jesus Christ never claimed to actually have died.

10. Whom did Paul describe as being "dead" in their sins?

    a) the Jews of Jerusalem
    b) the Romans
    c) his own traveling companions
    d) the Ephesian and Colossian believers

Dreams and Visions

1. Because King Abimelech inadvertently took Sarah, thinking she was Abraham's sister, what did God label him in a dream?

    a) a scourge
    b) an abomination
    c) an adulterer
    d) a dead man

2. Where did Jacob have his dream about the ladder to heaven?

    a) Bethel
    b) Zion
    c) Beulah
    d) Gad

3. What dreamer's self-aggrandizing visions got him sold into slavery?

4. Pharaoh dreamed about seven fat cows and seven lean cows. What did the cows do to one another in the dream?

    a) the fat cows ate all the pasture grass so that the lean cows died
    b) the fat cows ate the lean cows
    c) the lean cows ate the fat cows
    d) the lean cows contaminated the fat cows with something like hoof-and-mouth disease

5. The Preacher in Ecclesiastes cautions that in "the multitude of dreams and many words [empty promises] there are . . .":

    a) paths leading to perdition
    b) seeds of death
    c) signs of the serpent
    d) divers vanities

6. This prophet's vision of aerial faces and wheels inspired a latter-day gospel folksong and speculation concerning ancient UFOs.

    a) Jeremiah
    b) Ezekiel
    c) Daniel
    d) Haggai

7. Daniel correctly interpreted whose dreams?

   a) Meshach's
   b) King Nebuchadnezzar's
   c) King Jehoiakim's
   d) King Belshazzar's

8. Daniel correctly interpreted the handwriting on the wall that spelled King Belshazzar's doom—*mene, mene, tekel, upharsin*—to mean:

   a) numbered, weighed, divided
   b) tried, convicted, condemned
   c) monster, idolator, deceiver
   d) monster, idolator, corpse

9. At Jesus' trial, who, because of a disturbing dream, warned Pilate against prosecuting Him?

   a) Herod
   b) the centurion
   c) the chief priest's wife
   d) Pilate's wife

10. Peter had a vision of a sheet being lowered from heaven. The sheet was filled with _____.

   a) animals
   b) saints
   c) angels
   d) manna

The Early Church

1. Acts 3 speaks of:

   a) Peter's release from prison
   b) Paul's release from prison
   c) Timothy's release from prison
   d) Christ's second coming

2. This Roman ruler ordered Jews to leave the city of Rome.

   a) Aquila
   b) Claudius
   c) Herod
   d) Nero

3. The pagan goddess Diana (Artemis) caused great confusion at
   _____ .

   a) Rome
   b) Ephesus
   c) Thessalonica
   d) Colosse

4. Why was the Roman army commander in Jerusalem frightened
   after he ordered the beating of Paul?

   a) an angel condemned him
   b) it caused an uncontrollable riot
   c) he realized he was punishing an innocent citizen
   d) he learned Paul was a Roman citizen

5. Paul declared he was sent to preach, not to _____ .

   a) convert
   b) heal
   c) baptize
   d) Paul made no such statement

6. Paul told the Corinthians that women should cover their heads
   when praying or prophesying. What about men?

   a) they, too, should cover their heads
   b) they should not cover their heads
   c) they should cover their heads when praying but not when
      prophesying
   d) he said nothing about men's dress

7. Euodias and Syntyche apparently were squabbling, prompting
   Paul's rebuff. To which early church did they belong?

   a) Galatia
   b) Ephesus
   c) Philippi
   d) Rome

8. Who did the Philippians send to attend to the imprisoned Paul?

   a) Timothy
   b) Epaphroditus
   c) Philemon
   d) Silas

9. Visiting Paul on behalf of the Corinthians were Stephanas, Fortunatus, and _____.

   a) Philemon
   b) Aeneas
   c) Hanun
   d) Achaicus

10. Paul encouraged unity in the early church, stressing "one _____, one _____, one _____, one God and Father of all."

   a) Lord/faith/baptism
   b) Christ/intercessor/commission
   c) Spirit/truth/light
   d) hope/Word/doctrine

Ears to Hear

1. What Old Testament patriarch gathered his people's earrings and other "strange gods" and hid them under a tree near Shechem?

   a) Abraham
   b) Jacob
   c) Moses
   d) David

2. Old Testament law called for a hole to be drilled in the ear of _____.

   a) a man caught in adultery
   b) a woman caught in adultery
   c) a runaway slave who was caught
   d) a slave who intentionally forfeited freedom

3. Why did Aaron gather up the gold earrings of the women and children of Israel?

   a) because God denounced jewelry as being idolatrous
   b) to melt them and forge a golden calf
   c) as an offering to God
   d) to redistribute wealth

4. Old Testament law forbade the _____ of a deaf person.

    a) cursing
    b) enslavement
    c) marriage
    d) taxing

5. "They have ears, but they hear not: noses have they, but they smell not . . ." Who was the writer talking about in Psalm 115?

6. "[T]hou art unto them as a very lovely song of one that hath a pleasant voice . . . for they hear thy words, but they do them not." What prophet said that about the sinful people of Jerusalem?

    a) Isaiah
    b) Ezekiel
    c) Hosea
    d) Amos

7. How, specifically, did Jesus heal the deaf man at Decapolis?

    a) by filling the man's ears with a paste of clay and spittle
    b) by putting His fingers in the man's ears and speaking a command
    c) by commanding an evil spirit to leave the man
    d) by having the man submerge himself in the Sea of Galilee

8. In his zeal to protect Jesus, Peter cut off someone's ear. Where did this happen?

9. Paul told the Romans "_____ cometh by hearing, and hearing by the word of God."

    a) understanding
    b) light
    c) faith
    d) salvation

10. James wrote that everyone should be "swift to hear, slow to _____, slow to _____."

    a) anger/punish
    b) argue/judge
    c) curse/complain
    d) speak/wrath

Eyes to See

1. After Eve and Adam ate of the forbidden fruit, their eyes were opened to _____.
   - a) wisdom
   - b) God's physical presence
   - c) their nakedness
   - d) Satan's serpentine disguise

2. These two patriarchs are reported to have had failing eyesight as they approached death.
   - a) Adam and Noah
   - b) Noah and Abraham
   - c) Abraham and Benjamin
   - d) Isaac and Jacob

3. True or False: By Old Testament law, blindness disqualified a man from service as a temple priest.

4. True or False: By Old Testament law, blindness disqualified an animal from being sacrificed to the Lord.

5. True or False: The Lord momentarily restored Samson's eyesight so he could destroy the Philistines in their pagan temple.

6. Who placed a curse on "he that maketh the blind to wander out of the way"?
   - a) God through Moses
   - b) God through a psalmist
   - c) God through Isaiah
   - d) Jesus

7. The psalmist declares, "The eyes of the Lord are upon the _____."
   - a) wicked
   - b) downtrodden
   - c) repentant
   - d) righteous

8. Who ordered that King Zedekiah be blinded?
   - a) Jeremiah
   - b) Gedaliah
   - c) Ahikam
   - d) Nebuchadnezzar

9. This blind man, son of Timaeus, called on Jesus as "thou son of David" and was healed.

    a) Sered
    b) Bartimaeus
    c) Malcam
    d) Tahrea

10. What was the physical cause of Saul/Paul's temporary blindness?

    a) Jesus' brilliant light
    b) clay that covered his eyes
    c) something like scales that covered his eyes
    d) a stroke

Faith and Trust

1. When this king beseeched the Lord's help in faith, God delivered Judah from "a thousand thousand" Ethiopian invaders.

    a) Asa
    b) Abijah
    c) Jeroboam
    d) Ahiziah

2. Psalm 118:8—which some sources calculate to be the numerically central verse of the Bible—has what to say about trust?

3. Through Isaiah, God promised that "he that putteth his trust in me shall _____."

    a) conquer Satan
    b) possess the land
    c) enjoy long life
    d) overcome the fire

4. Jesus told his disciples if they had faith just the size of a _____, they could move a mountain.

    a) grain of sand
    b) grain of salt
    c) mustard seed
    d) corn kernel

5. When Thomas finally believed Jesus had risen from the dead, what did he say to affirm it?

    a) "Thou surely art He, the Messiah."
    b) "Why did I doubt?"
    c) "I have sinned."
    d) "My Lord and my God."

6. At the end of Mark's gospel account, Jesus states: "He that believeth and is baptized shall be saved; but he that believeth not shall be _____."

7. Paul told the Romans it was faith that had made this patriarch right with God.

    a) Adam
    b) Noah
    c) Abraham
    d) David

8. In his letter to the Ephesians, Paul likens faith to a _____.

    a) shield
    b) sword
    c) grain of sand
    d) mighty mountain

9. In the closing of his first letter to Timothy, Paul likens faith to a _____.

    a) saving grace
    b) ship's anchor
    c) good fight
    d) mountain

10. True or False: The rich cannot enter into the kingdom of God.

Famous Phrases

1. "[F]or they shall see eye to eye . . ." Who are "they" in this prophesy of Isaiah?

    a) kings
    b) warriors
    c) watchmen
    d) the people of Israel

2. "There were giants in the earth . . ." According to Scripture, they lived:

    a) before Adam and Eve
    b) before the great flood
    c) in Egypt
    d) in Philistia

3. Who escaped "by the skin of his teeth"?

    a) Jacob
    b) Moses
    c) David
    d) Job

4. Who was the first person named in Scripture literally to live "to a good old age"?

    a) Methuselah
    b) Noah
    c) Abraham
    d) Joshua

5. Abraham Lincoln's reference to "a house divided against itself" came from what part of the Bible?

    a) Genesis, concerning the dispute between Abraham and Lot
    b) Exodus, concerning the discontented people of Israel in the wilderness
    c) 1 Kings, concerning the rebellious sons of David
    d) the Gospels, concerning the accusation that Jesus was devil-ridden

6. Jesus Himself told the story of the "lost sheep." Who were his audience?

    a) the Pharisees and the scribes
    b) the multitude at the Sermon on the Mount
    c) His disciples
    d) children

7. In the Acts, what did Ananias, Sapphira, and Herod have in common?

    a) they were "as peas in a pod"
    b) they were "as the pot that calleth the kettle black"
    c) they all "gave up the ghost"
    d) they all refused to follow the "straight and narrow"

8. Who was "absent in body, but present in spirit"?

    a) Moses
    b) Elijah
    c) Jesus
    d) Paul

9. Which prophet spoke of "sour grapes"?

    a) Ezekiel
    b) Micah
    c) Habakkuk
    d) Zephaniah

10. What people first were said to live off "the fat of the land"?

    a) Noah and his family
    b) Jacob and his family
    c) the Moabites
    d) the Sodomites

Fire and Water

1. How long did it take the water to recede from the great flood?

    a) two months
    b) five months
    c) eight months
    d) ten months

2. Because the captive Israelites were multiplying so rapidly, Pharaoh issued what decree?

    a) that their God be honored by having each captive baptized
    b) that their God be honored by having each Egyptian baptized
    c) that newborn Israelite males be drowned in the Nile
    d) that newborn Israelite males be drowned in the Jordan

3. Which sinful Israelite king, seeing his doom was imminent, committed suicide by setting fire to his own palace?

    a) Elah
    b) Zimri
    c) Saul
    d) Amaziah

4. How many people were cast into a fiery furnace with Daniel?
   a) two
   b) three
   c) four
   d) zero

5. "As coals are to burning coals, and wood to fire," Proverbs states, "so is _____ to kindle strife."
   a) idle gossip
   b) a lie
   c) the decree of an evil king
   d) a contentious man

6. Which king burned the scroll containing God's words to Jeremiah?
   a) Jehoiakim
   b) Josiah
   c) Zedekiah
   d) Coniah

7. King Nebuchadnezzar was so furious at Shadrach, Meshach, and Abednego that he ordered their furnace of execution heated seven times hotter than normal. The result:
   a) the prisoners glowed white hot
   b) the flesh was scorched off the prisoners' faces before the guards could even cast them in
   c) the guards were killed by the blaze, though the prisoners survived
   d) the temple caught fire

8. Where was Jesus when he spoke to the Samaritan woman of God's "living water"?
   a) Sea of Galilee
   b) River Jordan
   c) Jacob's well
   d) a well at Rabbah

9. Where can you find the story of a waterlogged sacrifice?

10. This man washed his hands to signify he had no part in another person's death.
    a) Cain
    b) Moses
    c) Pilate
    d) Paul

Fish and Ships

1. Whom did God specifically designate to be navigator of Noah's ark?

   a) Himself
   b) Noah
   c) Shem
   d) no one

2. In his deathbed talk with his sons, Jacob pronounced that which of them would settle near the sea and be a "haven for ships"?

   a) Gad
   b) Isachar
   c) Simeon
   d) Zebulon

3. King Solomon's ships of _____ brought him gold, silver, ivory, apes, and peacocks every three years.

   a) Joppa
   b) Tarshish
   c) Sidon
   d) Dor

4. In reproving Job, the Lord mentioned what two methods of fishing, suggestive that they apparently were common in those times?

   a) nets and hooks
   b) nets and spears
   c) harpoons and nets
   d) harpoons and spears

5. One of the prophets described fishing methods thus: "They take up all of them with the angle, they catch them in the net, and gather them in their drag." Which prophet?

   a) Obadiah
   b) Nahum
   c) Habakkuk
   d) Haggai

6. Isaiah 19 forecast poor fishing in what country?

   a) Egypt
   b) Phoenicia
   c) Persia
   d) Macedonia

7. Ezekiel predicted this city would be laid flat, its site useful only for spreading and drying fishnets.

    a) Dor
    b) Tyrus
    c) Joppa
    d) Ashdod

8. After His resurrection, Jesus appeared to Peter and several others and told them where to fish. In what body of water were they fishing?

    a) Dead Sea
    b) Mediterranean Sea
    c) Sea of Tiberias
    d) River Jordan

9. How many fish did His followers catch after following Jesus' instructions?

    a) a netful; number not specified
    b) 87
    c) 153
    d) 896

10. On what body of water was Paul shipwrecked?

    a) Sea of Galilee
    b) River Jordan
    c) Aegean Sea
    d) Adriatic Sea

Food and Drink
I

1. In Genesis, God condemned the snake to a life of crawling, contempt, and a permanent diet of _____.

2. God fed the wandering Israelites by raining _____ from heaven.

    a) figs
    b) bread
    c) wheat
    d) fish

3. Some time after Samson killed a lion with his bare hands, he returned to the scene and removed from the carcass _____ to eat.

    a) maggots
    b) ants
    c) honey
    d) sun-dried flesh

4. Ruth clearly was favored when she was invited by Boaz at dinner to dip her bread in _____.

    a) olive oil
    b) a dish of dry spices
    c) butter
    d) vinegar

5. Miraculously sustained with unending supplies of meal and oil was the poor widow of _____.

    a) Gilead
    b) Shiloh
    c) Cherith
    d) Zarephath

6. Proverbs describes wine as a _____.

    a) balm
    b) two-edged sword
    c) medicine
    d) mocker

7. When John the Baptist preached in the Judaean wilderness, he ate _____ and _____.

8. Jesus miraculously fed the multitude with _____ and _____.

    a) bread and wine
    b) wine and cheese
    c) loaves and fishes
    d) milk and honey

9. Christ's body is symbolized by _____.

    a) grapes
    b) bread
    c) mutton
    d) honey

10. Just before Jesus' death on the cross, Roman guards offered Him
_____ to drink.

    a) water
    b) oil
    c) blood
    d) vinegar

Food and Drink
II

1. God forbade this individual from eating any meat that still had blood in it.

    a) Adam
    b) Noah
    c) Isaac
    d) Jacob

2. Who was the first person in the Bible to get drunk?

    a) Eve
    b) Noah
    c) Lot
    d) King David

3. God told His people they could eat any kind of seafood that had

_____ .

    a) gills
    b) scales
    c) gills and scales
    d) fins and scales

4. Which of the following birds (among others) did God specifically prohibit His people from eating?

    a) raven
    b) robin
    c) sparrow
    d) all of the above

5. True or False: God told the Israelites it was okay to eat certain flying insects.

6. When David was in hiding, Ahimelech the priest gave him bread to eat. What was special about this food?

7. "[T]hirty measures of fine flour, and threescore measures of meal, ten fat oxen, and twenty oxen out of the pastures, and an hundred sheep, beside harts, and roebucks, and fallowdeer, and fatted fowl." This was the "provision for one day" in whose abode?

   a) Pharaoh's
   b) Solomon's
   c) Nebuchadnezzar's
   d) Herod's

8. Elisha purified the sickening spring water at Jericho with
   _____ .

   a) honey
   b) sugar
   c) salt
   d) vinegar

9. The prophet Ezekiel and the apostle John both "ate God's Word," devouring scrolls. What did the Word of God literally taste like?

   a) fish
   b) lamb
   c) milk
   d) honey

10. True or False: The Bible refers to tomatoes as poisonous.

Food and Drink
III

1. While languishing in the wilderness, the children of Israel bewailed the lavish fare they had enjoyed while captives in Egypt: fish, cucumbers, melons, leeks, _____ , and
   _____ .

   a) leavened bread and milk
   b) unleavened bread and milk
   c) onions and garlic
   d) red wine and mutton

2. To appease angry David after her husband's insult, Abigail presented David and his soldiers with, among other items, 200 _____ and 200 _____.

    a) fish/gourds of milk
    b) fat calves/gourds of milk
    c) loaves of bread/bottles of wine
    d) loaves of bread/fig cakes

3. After Saul's unhappy interview with the Witch of Endor, she prepared him a meal. What did she serve?

    a) bread and wine
    b) pork, root vegetables, and pineapple
    c) fish
    d) veal and unleavened bread

4. What king is known to have eaten off gold dishes?

    a) Solomon
    b) Nebuchadnezzar
    c) Herod
    d) all of the above

5. Elisha instructed a creditor-plagued widow to borrow these kitchen items from her neighbors.

    a) potatoes
    b) empty jars
    c) wine skins
    d) plates

6. What did Elisha do to remedy a foul-tasting stew?

    a) added milk and honey
    b) added unspecified herbs
    c) added meal
    d) nothing—he warned that it was poisoned and must be thrown away

7. Because of King Manesseh's evil reign, God vowed to:

    a) wipe Jerusalem as a man wipeth a dish
    b) boil the evil king in ox fat
    c) stab Judah as with a fork
    d) roast his wicked kingdom over the fire of trial

8. Job spoke of the time when his steps were "washed . . . with butter." This signified that:

   a) he lacked meat and bread
   b) he had plenty of everything
   c) he was wasteful, provoking the Lord's punishment
   d) his enemies set traps for him

9. As comfort food for the lovesick, Solomon prescribed flagons (raisins) and _____.

   a) shellfish
   b) beans
   c) apples
   d) honey

10. What prophet referred to sinful Israel as, essentially, a "half-baked" pastry?

   a) Daniel
   b) Hosea
   c) Jonah
   d) Haggai

The Garden of Eden

1. Four river branches watered the Garden of Eden. Name two of them.

2. God put Adam in the Garden of Eden for this specific purpose.

   a) for protection from outside dangers
   b) to tend the garden
   c) to label all the plant and animal species
   d) for pure enjoyment

3. When He placed Adam in the garden, the Lord gave him a command and a warning concerning _____.

   a) the Sabbath
   b) poisonous snakes
   c) food
   d) strong drink

4. What was the forbidden tree?

    a) tree of darkness and despair
    b) tree of knowledge of good and evil
    c) tree of light
    d) tree of death

5. Why did God put Adam into a deep sleep?

6. God walked through His garden at what time of day?

7. Angered at Adam and Eve's disobedience, God cursed
   _____.

    a) Adam and Eve
    b) the sun
    c) the ground
    d) all creation

8. Before the fall, what did Adam and Eve use to make their clothing?

    a) fig leaves
    b) animal hides
    c) a type of garment believed to have been woven of cotton
    d) nothing

9. When He banished Adam and Eve from the garden, how did God clothe them?

    a) with fig leaves
    b) with cotton fibers sewn by the angel Michael
    c) with animal skin coats
    d) He didn't; He sent them away naked and they made their own clothes

10. In sealing the Garden of Eden after expelling Adam and Eve, what was God's objective?

    a) to protect the wildlife therein from sinful humans
    b) to thwart human access to the tree of life
    c) to preserve the garden as an unblemished monument to His work
    d) to protect Adam and Eve and their descendants from the serpent

Gifts

1. What son presented his father with a meal of savory wild game, hoping for a blessing that never came?

2. After leaving Laban, as Jacob and his host approached the land of Seir, Jacob sent a large herd of choice livestock ahead as a present to whom?
   - a) Isaac
   - b) Esau
   - c) Abimelech
   - d) Hamor

3. To appease the governor in Egypt (unwittingly, his own son Joseph), Jacob sent his older sons back to Egypt with presents of balm, honey, spices, myrrh, and a specific type of nut:
   - a) walnuts
   - b) pecans
   - c) cashews
   - d) almonds

4. In Leviticus 26, God promises His people gifts of seasonal rain, ample harvests, dominion over their enemies, and His guidance and protection . . . IF:
   - a) "ye sacrifice the first tenth of everything ye possess to my name"
   - b) "ye walk in my statutes, and keep my commandments, and do them"
   - c) "ye go where I shall lead ye"
   - d) "ye obey the commands of my servant Joshua"

5. Two hundred loaves, two bottles of wine, five dressed sheep, five measures of parched corn, raisins, fig cakes . . . Who offered this food as atonement to disgruntled David's fugitive band?
   - a) Saul
   - b) Jonathan
   - c) Abigail
   - d) Nabal

6. King Hiram gave Solomon fine cedar and fir trees, as well as gold, during the building of the great temple. In return, what did Solomon give Hiram?

    a) a share of ownership in the temple
    b) a suite in the royal palace
    c) 90,000 head of livestock
    d) twenty cities in Galilee

7. At the end of Job's tribulations, his relatives and old friends gave him _____.

    a) silverware
    b) silos filled with food
    c) gold earrings and money
    d) grain and livestock

8. Daniel said God gives "_____ unto the wise, and _____ to them that know understanding."

    a) wisdom/knowledge
    b) many children/long life
    c) silver/precious stones
    d) living water/peace

9. What gifts did the wise men bring the baby Jesus?

10. What gift does Jesus offer "all ye that labor and are heavy laden"?

    a) prosperity
    b) long life
    c) wisdom
    d) rest

God's Commandments

1. What was one of the commands God gave Moses from the burning bush?

    a) to sacrifice his son
    b) to carve the Ten Commandments in stone
    c) to build an altar of quartz
    d) to take off his shoes

2. God issued the Ten Commandments to the Israelites through
   _____.

   a) Noah
   b) Abraham
   c) Moses
   d) Samuel

3. Besides Exodus 20, in what other book and chapter of the Bible
   do we find the Ten Commandments?

4. God during the Exodus specifically forbade His people from
   harming or cheating a stranger (foreigner). What unique reason
   did He give?

   a) the Israelites might be entertaining angels unaware
   b) they needed to make friends with everyone they met
   c) foreigners, while not "neighbors," nonetheless deserved
      respect
   d) the Israelites had been foreigners themselves in the land
      of Egypt

5. God told the Israelites that if they found the carcass of wild game
   killed by other animals, they must:

   a) cast it to the dogs
   b) eat it before it spoiled
   c) build an altar on the spot and sacrifice the flesh
   d) mark the spot and not return there for three generations

6. "Go, make of all disciples" is known as _____.

   a) The Atonement
   b) The Great Commission
   c) The Incarnation
   d) The Fourth Beatitude

7. What did Jesus say is the law's greatest commandment?

8. From which Old Testament book did Jesus repeat this command?

   a) Genesis
   b) Exodus
   c) Leviticus
   d) Deuteronomy

9. What did Jesus say is the law's second-greatest commandment?

10. From which Old Testament book did Jesus repeat this second command?

    a) Genesis
    b) Exodus
    c) Leviticus
    d) Deuteronomy

God's Enemies

1. Where did Cain go to live after God banished him from Eden?

2. Very quickly after the Philistines captured the Ark of the Covenant, they realized it was the last thing they wanted or needed. How did God make that clear to them?

    a) He destroyed their god Dagon
    b) He destroyed their god Dagon and slew the firstborn of every Philistine family
    c) He destroyed their god Dagon and smote the Philistines with emerods, or tumors
    d) He destroyed their god Dagon and their city of Ekron

3. What became of wicked Jezebel's corpse?

    a) it was given a royal burial
    b) it was buried in a pauper's grave
    c) it was destroyed in an accidental fire
    d) dogs ate it

4. In a reference to Esther's adversary, American criminals of the 19th and early 20th centuries were admonished that if convicted, they would "hang higher than _____."

5. After Daniel survived the lions' den, King Darius ordered Daniel's accusers thrown to the lions instead. Darius likewise condemned what other individuals to the den?

    a) his soothsayers
    b) three of his wives
    c) the families of Daniel's accusers
    d) his master-at-arms

6. Jesus referred to King Herod as a _____.

    a) fox
    b) devil
    c) badger
    d) lunatic

7. The Epicureans and Stoicks in Athens ridiculed Paul, calling him a _____.

    a) Jew
    b) babbler
    c) lunatic
    d) foreigner

8. Herod Agrippa listened to Paul's defense alongside a woman named _____.

    a) Jezebel
    b) Alice
    c) Herodias
    d) Bernice

9. What was the end of Herod Agrippa I, who persecuted the early church, had James executed, and had Peter arrested?

    a) he was crucified by his own soldiers
    b) he was struck by lightning
    c) he was struck down by an angel of the Lord and was devoured by worms
    d) he drowned

10. In 2 Thessalonians, what do Paul and his companions warn will happen at Jesus' second coming to people who have rejected God?

    a) Jesus will forgive them and welcome them to heaven
    b) God will give them a place in heaven a little lower than that of the saints
    c) God will commit them to purgatory for varying lengths of incarceration, then accept them into heaven
    d) they will be banished and punished forever

God's Love

1. In Deuteronomy, we learn that God will keep His "covenant and mercy with them that love him and keep his commandments" for how many generations?

    a) 6
    b) 20
    c) 490
    d) 1,000

2. In the 23rd Psalm, the Lord is likened to what type of caregiver?

3. The psalmist sang that "because thy lovingkindness is better than _____, my lips shall praise thee."

   a) manna
   b) honey
   c) gold and satin
   d) life

4. "Oh that men would praise the Lord for his goodness, and for his wonderful works to the children of men!" This tribute to God's love occurs four times in one chapter of which book?

   a) Leviticus
   b) Psalms
   c) Isaiah
   d) Revelation

5. "As one whom his mother comforteth, so will I comfort you . . ." God promised His people that through _____.

   a) Isaiah
   b) Ezekiel
   c) Zechariah
   d) Jesus

6. Malachi asserted that God had demonstrated His love for His people by:

   a) spawning them from Noah's lineage after the flood
   b) loving Jacob while hating Esau
   c) delivering them from Egyptian bondage
   d) delivering Jericho and Ai into their hands

7. The supreme promise to Christians, given by Jesus in John 3:16, is that God loved the world so much He gave us what?

8. God knows and loves each of us so well, Jesus said, that He can tell:

   a) our every thought
   b) the number of cells in our bodies
   c) the number of hairs on our heads
   d) the exact age of each individual, down to the minute

9. Because God cares for us, Peter wrote in his first epistle, we can:

   a) ignore some of the Old Testament regulations
   b) expect forgiveness whenever we sin
   c) see paradise
   d) cast all our cares on Him

10. According to the apostle John, "this is the love of God":
    a) that we love our enemies
    b) that we keep his commandments
    c) that we believe that Jesus is the Christ
    d) that we be baptized by water and the Holy Spirit

God's Modus Operandi
I

1. After the great flood, how did God clear away the waters?

2. What means did God use to part the Red Sea waters so His people could escape from Egypt?
    a) a drought
    b) a gigantic fireball—possibly a comet
    c) a fault in the earth's crust
    d) wind

3. What means did God use to cause the boils he sent to plague the Egyptians who held the Israelites hostage?
    a) ashes
    b) sand
    c) rain
    d) the sun's rays

4. No one on earth can see God in person and live. Therefore, God revealed to Moses only part of His _____.
    a) ear
    b) palm
    c) arm
    d) back

5. In which book does the Bible say God helps those who help themselves?

6. God did not let Elijah die, but transported him bodily to heaven via a _____.
    a) carriage of gold
    b) whirlwind
    c) ladder of woven vines
    d) gigantic bird

7. When God was ready for His captive people to return to Jerusalem and rebuild His temple, He moved the heart of this pagan king to let them do so.

    a) Xerxes
    b) Artaxerxes
    c) Alexander
    d) Cyrus

8. How did God arrange for Esther to become queen?

    a) by threatening King Ahasuerus with death if he didn't marry Esther
    b) by having Queen Vashti executed
    c) in a beauty contest
    d) all of the above

9. Proverbs teaches that if we don't punish our children when they do wrong, we're demonstrating what?

    a) love for our children
    b) hatred for our children
    c) forgiveness for our children
    d) patience and godliness

10. Just before Jesus was born, God's angel promised a son to the aging Zacharias and his wife Elisabeth. When Zacharias expressed disbelief, how did God punish him?

    a) He withdrew the promise of a son
    b) He delayed the birth
    c) He decided Zacharias would not live to see his son's birth
    d) He temporarily struck Zacharias dumb

God's Modus Operandi
II

1. Why did God put Adam in the Garden of Eden?

    a) to tend it
    b) to enjoy it as his earthly paradise
    c) to establish dominion over all the creatures God had created
    d) to test Adam's obedience

2. Before Cain killed his brother, what did Cain do to provoke God's reprimand?

   a) cursed the land God had given him
   b) cursed Abel
   c) made an unworthy offering to God
   d) lied about his activities

3. God declared Abraham righteous and made him the leader of His people because of _____.

   a) Abraham's lineage
   b) Abraham's pledge to obey God's laws
   c) Abraham's faith
   d) all of the above

4. Why did the Lord separate the people into different language groups?

   a) because of the sins of Sodom and Gomorrah
   b) because they were building a monument toward heaven
   c) to differentiate the twelve tribes of Israel
   d) to separate Israel from the other nations

5. Why did God let Joseph be sent into slavery in Egypt?

   a) to fulfill Joseph's prophetic, self-aggrandizing dreams
   b) to humiliate his brothers
   c) to punish his father Jacob
   d) so Joseph eventually could save God's people from starvation

6. Because he found himself standing on holy ground at Mt. Sinai, Moses was commanded by God to:

   a) cover his face so he wouldn't be blinded
   b) kneel
   c) put on his shoes
   d) take off his shoes

7. God killed Aaron's sons Nadab and Abihu by fire because they did something wrong. What was their guilt?

   a) burning incense improperly
   b) crafting a silver idol
   c) crafting a gold idol
   d) conspiring against Moses' leadership

8. Why did God desert King Saul?

   a) because Saul was jealous of David and tried to kill him
   b) because Saul allied himself with the king of Philistia
   c) because Saul did not totally destroy the Amalekites as God had commanded
   d) because Saul in a rage cursed Samuel

9. Uzzah the cart driver was struck dead because he:

   a) transported King Saul into hiding from David
   b) touched the sacred Ark of the Covenant
   c) cursed the Lord
   d) defiled King David's daughter

10. True or False: Job's troubles resulted from a challenge Satan issued to God.

God's Wrath

1. After driving Adam and Eve from the Garden of Eden, the Lord guarded the sacred place with cherubims and a _____.

   a) flaming sword
   b) poisonous serpent
   c) perpetual flame
   d) bottomless moat

2. Whom did God turn into a pillar of salt because of an act of disobedience at the destruction of Sodom and Gomorrah?

3. Because the Israelites in their wandering refused to obey God, He decreed that none of the adult men who had escaped from Egypt would see the promised land—with two faithful exceptions: Joshua and _____.

4. God vowed that Eli's sons Hophni and Phinehas would die together because of their wickedness. How did they die?

   a) drowned in a flood
   b) hanged by King Saul's soldiers
   c) poisoned by a servant at a banquet
   d) killed in battle by the Philistines

5. Elijah forbade the rain because of God's anger toward
   _____.

   a) the Philistines
   b) the Edomites
   c) King Ahab
   d) King Omri

6. What king did God send to destroy Jerusalem?

   a) Abimelech
   b) Nebuchadnezzar
   c) Jehoiachin
   d) Cyrus

7. The wages of sin, Paul warned, is _____.

8. In the last days, God's wrath will be so overwhelming that people will:

   a) be literally paralyzed with fear
   b) beg the rocks and mountains to fall on them and hide them
   c) leap from cliffs to escape it
   d) plunge into the River Jordan to escape it

9. In the last days, those who "worship the beast and his image, and receive his mark" will be:

   a) tormented with fire and brimstone
   b) cast to the lions
   c) cast to the ravenous dogs
   d) saved only if they repent

10. "For the great day of his wrath is come; and who shall be able to stand?" Who made this dramatic prophesy?

    a) Solomon
    b) Joel
    c) Jesus
    d) John

Go Where I Send Thee

1. God told Abraham His people would go to a strange land (Egypt) and languish there approximately _____ years.

    a) 4
    b) 40
    c) 400
    d) 4,000

2. Angry at the Israelites for abandoning His ways, the Lord made them wander in the wilderness for _____ years.

3. God at first forbade the soothsayer Balaam from going to this place to curse the Israelites—then sent him there to praise the Israelites.

    a) Mesopotamia
    b) Moab
    c) Egypt
    d) Galatia

4. God commanded Jonah to go preach in _____.

    a) Tarshish
    b) Nineveh
    c) Joppa
    d) Philistia

5. When the ship crew realized Jonah's presence was the cause of the stormy sea, whose idea was it to throw him overboard?

    a) Jonah's
    b) the ship captain's
    c) a passenger's, the prophet Obadiah
    d) a passenger's, the prophet Nahum

6. How long was Jonah in the stomach of the fish?

7. What did Jonah do inside the fish's belly?

    a) slept in a coma
    b) wept
    c) prayed
    d) the Bible does not say

8. "Let us go into Judea again." When Jesus told His disciples that upon hearing of Lazarus' illness, why did they resist?

    a) because of the distance
    b) because word had arrived that Lazarus already was dead
    c) because some of them did not like Lazarus
    d) because it was in Judea that a mob had tried to stone Jesus

9. Paul generally was sent to preach to the _____.

    a) Jews
    b) Gentiles
    c) Philistines
    d) Ethiopians

10. As a prisoner, Paul was sent to Rome because:

    a) the high priest Ananias granted him an appeal to be heard there
    b) King Agrippa refused to hear his case
    c) the crimes he was accused of were against the Roman government
    d) he appealed to Caesar, as was his right as a Roman citizen

Grief

1. "Let me not see the death of the child," mourned this distraught outcast in the Beersheba wilderness as she sat down to die. Who was she?

2. Devastated by the loss of one son—with a second being held in apparent danger—this Old Testament patriarch tried to keep his youngest son in seclusion to avert further sorrow.

    a) Noah
    b) Jacob
    c) Moses
    d) Aaron

3. To his horror, Jephthah's victory over the Ammonites unwittingly cost him _____.

    a) his fortune
    b) his wife
    c) his daughter
    d) his life

4. An Old Testament priest mistook this person's profound grief for drunkenness.

    a) Esau's
    b) Rachel's
    c) Joseph's
    d) Hannah's

5. King David grieved terribly for these two sons, although their deaths resulted from their abominable sins against him and the royal family.

    a) Amnon and Absalom
    b) Amnon and Adonijah
    c) Absalom and Adonijah
    d) Adonijah and Solomon

6. "We hanged our harps upon the willows . . ." The Jewish people did not feel like making music, for they were deep in sorrow over what?

    a) forty years of wandering in the wilderness
    b) the death of King David
    c) the death of King Solomon
    d) their captivity in Babylon

7. Before raising a certain corpse from death, Jesus had to oust the wake musicians and other mourners who scoffed at Him. Who was the deceased?

8. After the death of John the Baptist, what did Jesus do?

    a) wept for many hours
    b) cried in anger to God
    c) went off in a boat to be alone
    d) leveled a curse at Herod

9. What made Peter cry bitterly?

    a) the death of Lazarus
    b) the death of Paul
    c) the death of James
    d) hearing the cock crow after his third denial of Christ

10. In heaven, "there shall be no more death, neither sorrow, nor crying, neither shall there be any more pain." Who said that?

    a) John the Baptist
    b) Paul
    c) Peter
    d) the apostle John

Heavenly Phenomena

1. Noah's descendants thought they could get to heaven literally by building a tower made of _____.

    a) granite
    b) bricks
    c) sand
    d) wood and stone

2. True or False: After the flood, Noah did not die but was taken to heaven alive on a winged chariot.

3. In discoursing with Job, God mentions two constellations by name. Name either of them.

4. "Therefore I will shake the heavens, and the earth shall remove out of her place, in the wrath of the Lord of hosts, and in the day of his fierce anger." This warning was given through whom?

    a) Noah
    b) Isaiah
    c) Ezekiel
    d) the apostle John

5. At one point in its waywardness, Israel was chastised by this prophet for worshipping star gods.

    a) Amos
    b) Obadiah
    c) Nahum
    d) Habakkuk

6. James and John wanted to call down fire from heaven to destroy the unfriendly people of this region, but Jesus refused.

    a) Caesarea
    b) Cana
    c) Gadara
    d) Samaria

7. Jesus said His second coming will be like _____ that comes from the east and shines to the west.

    a) sunlight
    b) the brightest star
    c) lightning
    d) a shower of brimstone

8. Who foretold that in the end times, "there shall be signs in the sun, and in the moon, and in the stars; and upon the earth distress of nations . . ."?

    a) Jeremiah
    b) Micah
    c) Jesus
    d) the apostle John

9. As Jesus hung dying on the cross, this heavenly phenomenon occurred.

    a) mysterious writing in red against a sky of grey clouds
    b) a fiery horse streaking across a stormy sky
    c) three hours of daytime darkness
    d) an apparent tornado that sucked the altar heavenward from the temple

10. At the Pentecost, Peter referenced an Old Testament prophet when he described "wonders in heaven above, and signs in the earth beneath; blood, and fire, and vapor of smoke." Which prophet provided the basis for that description?

    a) Jeremiah
    b) Daniel
    c) Hosea
    d) Joel

The Holy Spirit

1. "Can we find such a one as this is, a man in whom the spirit of God is?" What pagan leader said that about a descendant of Israel?

    a) Abimelech
    b) Pharaoh
    c) Nebuchadnezzar
    d) Belshazzar

2. When the Spirit of the Lord came over him, this man probably was the most lethal fighter of all time.

    a) Joshua
    b) Samson
    c) David
    d) Benaiah

3. John the Baptist foretold that Jesus would baptize with the Holy Spirit and what else?

   a) water
   b) peace
   c) fire
   d) war

4. Who referred to the Holy Spirit as a teacher?

   a) Jesus
   b) John
   c) Peter
   d) James

5. At Pentecost after Jesus' ascension, the Holy Spirit came to the disciples in a house. What sound did it make?

   a) a crackle, like a slow-burning fire
   b) a roar, like a scorching furnace
   c) a gentle whisper, like a breeze through tree tops
   d) that of a rushing mighty wind

6. Who tried to buy the power of the Holy Spirit with money?

   a) Saul
   b) Nebuchadnezzar
   c) Zacchaeus
   d) Simon of Samaria

7. After Timothy was accepted by the Jews and allowed to follow Paul, they considered traveling to these places to preach but were forbidden by the Holy Spirit.

   a) Tyre and Sidon
   b) Asia and Bithynia
   c) Macedonia and Crete
   d) Jerusalem and Nazareth

8. Paul listed nine fruits of the Spirit in his letter to the Galatians. Name five of them.

9. Paul told the Ephesians that through Christ, God gave us the Holy Spirit as _____.

   a) our intercessor
   b) the seal of His promise
   c) protection from specific diseases
   d) a symbol of His forgiveness

10. The Bible states that one Sabbath Day, the Spirit filled a certain man and prompted him to pen a book of Scripture. What man? What book?

   a) Solomon/Ecclesiastes
   b) Obadiah/Obadiah
   c) Luke/Acts
   d) John/Revelation

Husbands and Wives

1. Before Laban would give his daughter Rachel to Jacob in marriage, he tricked Jacob into marrying Rachel's older sister _____.

   a) Zilpah
   b) Bilhah
   c) Deborah
   d) Leah

2. In all, how long did Jacob have to work for Laban to earn his two wives?

   a) 14 days
   b) 14 weeks
   c) 140 days
   d) 14 years

3. True or False: Joseph, son of Jacob, took an Egyptian wife.

4. Whose wife was Zipporah?

   a) Simeon's
   b) Esau's
   c) Moses'
   d) David's

5. The widow Abigail, before marrying David, had been wife to a foolish man named _____.

6. When King David danced before the Lord, he was scorned by his wife _____.

   a) Inar
   b) Michal
   c) Bathsheba
   d) Bilhah

7. Which daughter of King Saul was promised to David but was given in marriage to another man instead?

    a) Inar
    b) Michal
    c) Delilah
    d) Merab

8. What was especially remarkable about King Solomon's 700 wives?

    a) they were all sisters or step-sisters
    b) they were all older than him
    c) they were all princesses
    d) they were all godly

9. In the first-century church, this couple died because they greedily withheld some of their land-dealing profits.

    a) Tobias and Lydia
    b) Joses and Winona
    c) Ananias and Sapphira
    d) Theudas and Gretchen

10. In his letter to the Ephesians, Paul asserted that husbands should love their wives just as _____.

    a) God loves the world
    b) Christ loves the church
    c) tax collectors love money
    d) they love themselves

Hymns
I

1. "Immortal, Invisible, God Only Wise." This hymn title is taken from what book of the Bible?

    a) Genesis
    b) Mark
    c) Ephesians
    d) 1 Timothy

2. "'Man of Sorrows,' What a Name" was suggested by what Old Testament prophet?

    a) Isaiah
    b) Ezekiel
    c) Daniel
    d) Amos

3. Which epistle of Paul inspired the theme "In the Cross of Christ I Glory"?

    a) 2 Corinthians
    b) Galatians
    c) 1 Thessalonians
    d) 2 Timothy

4. "Great Is Thy Faithfulness" was inspired by what book?

    a) Exodus
    b) Ezra
    c) Lamentations
    d) Ezekiel

5. "I Know That My Redeemer Liveth" stems from what book?

    a) Job
    b) Psalms
    c) 1 Corinthians
    d) Titus

6. "Holy, Holy, Holy, Lord God Almighty." One of the books in which this hymn title is found is:

    a) Genesis
    b) Psalms
    c) Matthew
    d) Revelation

7. "Let All Mortal Flesh Keep Silence" and the call to prayer "The Lord Is in His Holy Temple" are drawn from the same verse of what prophetic book?

    a) Jeremiah
    b) Ezekiel
    c) Habakkuk
    d) Zephaniah

8. This prophet inspired the adjective "little" in "O Little Town of Bethlehem."

    a) Micah
    b) Nahum
    c) Zephaniah
    d) Zechariah

9. "Rock of Ages, Cleft for Me" is a hymn title taken from what book?

    a) Genesis
    b) Exodus
    c) Proverbs
    d) Luke

10. "Worthy is the Lamb"—a phrase used in various hymn and praise song settings—comes from what book?

    a) Isaiah
    b) Zechariah
    c) Romans
    d) Revelation

Hymns
II

1. "Take Up Thy Cross and Follow Me" takes its title from which New Testament book?

    a) Mark
    b) Acts
    c) Romans
    d) Revelation

2. The opening lines of "Search Me, O God" are taken almost verbatim from what book?

    a) Genesis
    b) Psalms
    c) Luke
    d) 2 Peter

3. The praise song "Behold, What Manner of Love" comes directly from what epistle?

    a) Colossians
    b) 1 Peter
    c) 1 John
    d) 3 John

4. The title "There Shall Be Showers of Blessing" is taken verbatim from what book?

    a) Genesis
    b) Ezekiel
    c) Matthew
    d) Mark

5. The title of the traditional spiritual "There Is a Balm in Gilead" comes from what prophetic book?

    a) Isaiah
    b) Jeremiah
    c) Lamentations
    d) Nahum

6. "What Can Wash Away My Sins?" ("Nothing but the Blood of Jesus") is based on what epistle?

    a) Galatians
    b) 1 Timothy
    c) 1 Peter
    d) 1 John

7. The phrase "Thou art the Potter, I am the clay" from the hymn "Have Thine Own Way, Lord" comes from which prophet?

    a) Isaiah
    b) Daniel
    c) Jonah
    d) Zechariah

8. The early American folk hymn "Wayfaring Stranger" likely references the Bible verse: "I am a stranger in the earth: hide not thy commandments from me." Who made that statement?

    a) Jacob
    b) Moses
    c) the writer of the Bible's shortest Psalm
    d) the writer of the Bible's longest Psalm

9. The "mercy seat" in "From Every Stormy Wind That Blows" is referenced first in what book?

    a) Genesis
    b) Exodus
    c) Leviticus
    d) 1 Chronicles

10. The funereal hymn "Abide With Me" draws its title from a supplication in what book?

    a) Nehemiah
    b) Job
    c) Luke
    d) Acts

Kinfolk of the Old Testament
I

1. Cain and Abel had a number of siblings. One whose name is given in the Bible was their younger brother _____.

    a) Seth
    b) Mordred
    c) Manasseh
    d) Elimelech

2. Methuselah, the oldest person mentioned in the Bible, was what relation to Noah?

    a) father
    b) grandfather
    c) great-great grandfather
    d) none of the above

3. Who were the first twins named in the Bible?

4. The only other twins mentioned in the Bible, Pharez and Zarah, were sons of Judah and Tamar. Tamar was Judah's _____.

    a) sister
    b) sister-in-law
    c) daughter-in-law
    d) first cousin

5. Which of Joseph's brothers saved his life?

6. Name either of Naomi's two sons.

7. What was Ruth's relationship to Naomi?
    a) mother
    b) daughter
    c) daughter-in-law
    d) servant

8. How many older brothers did David have?

9. David's army general Joab was also his _____.
    a) nephew
    b) uncle
    c) brother
    d) cousin

10. How many generations separated Abraham from Jesus?
    a) twenty
    b) forty-two
    c) forty-nine
    d) sixty-four

Kinfolk of the Old Testament
II

1. Humiliated after the incident of his drunken nakedness, Noah cursed which of his grandsons?
    a) Japheth
    b) Shem
    c) Canaan
    d) Heth

2. What relation was Noah to the great hunter Nimrod?
    a) brother
    b) uncle
    c) first cousin
    d) great-grandfather

3. True or False: Abram/Abraham was of the lineage of Noah's son Japheth.

4. Who were Huz and Buz?

   a) nephews of Noah
   b) nephews of Abraham
   c) brothers of Joshua
   d) brothers of Job

5. After the death of Sarah and the marriage of his son Isaac, Abraham remarried. What was his new wife's name?

   a) Keturah
   b) Miriam
   c) Leah
   d) Elisabeth

6. When Abraham died, who buried him?

   a) his son Ishmael
   b) his sons Isaac and Ishmael
   c) his grandson Esau
   d) his grandsons Jacob and Esau

7. Jacob was twice related to Laban. He was Laban's
   _____ .

   a) cousin and brother-in-law
   b) cousin and son-in-law
   c) nephew and son-in-law
   d) brother-in-law and son-in-law

8. What was there about Leah's appearance that made her less attractive than her younger sister Rachel?

   a) she was fat
   b) she was thin
   c) she had weak eyes
   d) her hair was prematurely grey

9. Joshua was Moses' _____ .

   a) son
   b) grandson
   c) nephew
   d) no immediate relation

10. True or False: David and Jonathan were related.

Kinfolk of the New Testament

1. Who was younger: Jesus or His cousin John the Baptist?

2. The New Testament mentions four earthly brothers of Jesus. Name two of them.

3. Mary and Martha of Bethany had a brother who was the subject of one of Jesus' most astonishing miracles. What was his name?

4. Of which tribe of Israel was Paul descended?
   a) Judah
   b) Levi
   c) Benjamin
   d) Joseph

5. What was the relation between Lydia and Ananias?
   a) wife and husband
   b) sister and brother
   c) mother and son-in-law
   d) no known relation

6. John Mark's mother was an early Christian named
   _____.
   a) Drusilla
   b) Mary
   c) Rhoda
   d) Deborah

7. Because of John Mark's one-time act of desertion, his cousin _____ had a dramatic falling-out with Paul over whether to keep John Mark as their traveling companion.
   a) Silas
   b) Barnabas
   c) Timothy
   d) Titus

8. Timothy's parents were of what disparate nationalities?
   a) Jewish and Greek
   b) Jewish and Roman
   c) Persian and Macedonian
   d) Samaritan and Macedonian

9. What relative of Paul once exposed an assassination plot against him?

    a) brother
    b) wife
    c) sister
    d) nephew

10. This man's family were reported by Paul to be the first believers in Achaia (lower Greece).

    a) Achaiaus'
    b) Stephanas'
    c) Corolacas'
    d) Philemon's

Laws and Rituals

1. God instituted the Passover feast to remind His people of:

    a) Himself passing over the surface of the waters at creation
    b) His angel passing over the blood-marked homes of the captive Israelites when killing the Egyptians' firstborn
    c) the Israelites passing over the exposed riverbed in their flight from Egypt
    d) the heavenly dove passing over the scene of Jesus' baptism

2. True or False: In handing down the Old Testament law, God demanded that the Israelites present as an offering to Him "the first of the firstfruits."

3. True or False: God commanded the Israelites to destroy not only their own idols, but those of other people.

4. God specified to Moses during the Exodus the kinds of offerings His people were to bring to Him. Which of the following was not included?

    a) gold
    b) incense
    c) eagle wings
    d) goat hair

5. Old Testament law prescribed what as the penalty for breaking the Sabbath?

    a) death
    b) loss of an eye
    c) an elaborately detailed sacrifice of atonement
    d) nothing

6. Why did Moses break the stone tablets containing the Ten Commandments?

    a) an overwhelming sense of godly fear
    b) anger at the Israelites and their golden calf
    c) he was startled by a lightning bolt
    d) he stumbled on the rocky mountainside

7. The 50th year, as prescribed in Leviticus, was to be the Israelites' time of celebration called the Year of _____ .

    a) Cleansing
    b) Family
    c) Jubilee
    d) Holiness

8. In the laws of Deuteronomy, the Lord forbade His people from plowing _____ .

    a) with an ox and donkey yoked together
    b) in winter
    c) after sunset
    d) plots larger than two acres

9. In the laws of Deuteronomy, the Lord forbade His people from wearing _____ .

    a) clothes made of different materials in combination
    b) lambskin
    c) goatskin
    d) a headdress on the Sabbath

10. God did not forbid His people from dining on the Sabbath, but He forbade one ordinary household activity that substantially limited food preparation. What was it?

Leaders

I

1. Jacob died in Egypt but was buried in _____ .
    a) Edom
    b) Mesopotamia
    c) Canaan
    d) Midian

2. Who authorized the Feast of Purim?
    a) Moses
    b) Joshua
    c) Ahasuerus
    d) Mordecai and Esther

3. Proverbs 6 teaches that if people are wise and willing to work, they need no appointed commander. To illustrate, it points to which wild creature?

4. King David was of the tribe of Judah. His predecessor King Saul was of the tribe of _____ .
    a) Benjamin
    b) Reuben
    c) Levi
    d) Judah

5. The Queen of Sheba went to Jerusalem to quiz King _____ .
    a) Saul
    b) David
    c) Solomon
    d) Absalom

6. Nebuchadnezzar was _____ .
    a) king of Israel
    b) king of Judah
    c) king of Babylon
    d) king of Egypt

7. "If a ruler hearken to lies, all his servants are wicked." This warning was issued by _____ .

   a) Jesus
   b) Daniel
   c) Paul
   d) the writer of Proverbs

8. Jehoshaphat succeeded his father, Asa, as King of _____ .

   a) Judah
   b) Syria
   c) Assyria
   d) Tirzah

9. How did Moses die?

   a) unknown causes
   b) bitten by a cobra
   c) accidentally fell on Joshua's sword
   d) he didn't die; he was carried alive into heaven

10. Asked to resolve a dispute between two women who claimed to be mother of the same infant, what solution did King Solomon propose?

   a) make the women tread on hot coals to determine which was lying
   b) appoint a diviner to determine which was lying
   c) cut the child in two with a sword
   d) give the child to an adoptive mother

Leaders
II

1. Who was the first king of Israel?

   a) Eli
   b) Samuel
   c) Saul
   d) David

2. Which king led the defeat of the Philistines and brought the Ark of the Covenant to Jerusalem?

    a) Saul
    b) David
    c) Solomon
    d) Nebuchadnezzar

3. Which of David's sons temporarily seized the palace from his father in a coup?

    a) Amnon
    b) Absalom
    c) Adonijah
    d) Solomon

4. How did it happen that Solomon rather than his older brothers succeeded David as king?

    a) he was David's only legitimate son
    b) he killed all his older brothers
    c) Absalom, his only older brother who wanted to be king, died in a rebellion
    d) David promised him the throne

5. True or False: God proclaimed that Solomon would be the wisest person in all history.

6. Pleased with Solomon's request for wisdom, the Lord also gave him what two things he didn't request?

    a) long life and many children
    b) long life and many wives
    c) wealth and honor
    d) fame and glory

7. Over what kingdom was Jezebel queen?

    a) Babylon
    b) Philistia
    c) Judah
    d) Israel

8. True or False: Persian King Cyrus pillaged the Hebrews' temple; Babylonian King Nebuchadnezzar restored it.

9. The fifty-five-year reign of King Manasseh over the Israelites was most notable for its _____ .

    a) rebuilding of Jerusalem
    b) wicked return to idol worship
    c) warfare
    d) peace

10. Who sent Nehemiah to finish rebuilding Jerusalem?

    a) King Artaxerxes
    b) Samuel
    c) Solomon
    d) the apostle Paul

Light

1. True or False: The second thing God called for in creating the world was light.

2. What did the psalmist say is "a lamp unto my feet, and a light unto my path"?

    a) the sun by day, the moon by night
    b) God's Word
    c) God's love
    d) God's mercy

3. The Proverbs teach that "the commandment is a lamp, and the _____ is light."

    a) lamp
    b) Sabbath
    c) rod
    d) law

4. Isaiah prophesied that Israel would be a light to _____ .

    a) the poor and downtrodden
    b) the Gentiles
    c) the Romans
    d) the Greeks

5. Who was sent to Israel "to bear witness of the Light, that all men through him might believe"?

    a) Elijah
    b) Ezekiel
    c) John the Baptist
    d) Jesus

6. Evil doers hate the light, Jesus said. Who, on the other hand, did He say are drawn to the light?

   a) the meek
   b) the truthful
   c) the lost
   d) doers of good

7. Jesus said you should "let your light shine before men" so that:

   a) they could see wrong from right
   b) they could see forward from backward
   c) God would be glorified
   d) you would be glorified

8. What did Jesus say is the "light of the body"?

9. Who was surrounded by a light on the Damascus road?

   a) Mary Magdalene
   b) Jesus
   c) Saul/Paul
   d) Epaphroditus

10. Who referred to God as "the Father of lights, with whom is no variableness, neither shadow of turning."

    a) Isaiah
    b) Micah
    c) Peter
    d) James

$\mathcal{L}$ove

1. One of the problems with polygamy in the Old Testament is exemplified by the story of this patriarch. Married to two sisters, his overbearing love for the younger one resulted in unending jealousy.

   a) Abraham
   b) Lot
   c) Isaac
   d) Jacob

2. Old Testament law dictated that a man not be sent to war or other civic duties for how long after he married?

    a) a week
    b) a fortnight
    c) a moon, or month
    d) a year

3. The Proverbs teach that "hatred stirreth up strifes: but love _____."

    a) bringeth an end to strifes
    b) covereth all sins
    c) availeth much
    d) quincheth the thirst

4. During Jesus' earthly time, Jews refused to love—or even associate with—the _____ .

    a) Romans
    b) Greeks
    c) Samaritans
    d) Gentiles

5. In justifying the sinful woman's washing of His feet, Jesus told Simon the Pharisee that the person who _____ much loves much, but the person who _____ little loves little.

    a) repents
    b) sins
    c) understands
    d) is forgiven

6. "But I know you, that ye have not the love of God in you." Whom was Jesus accusing when He said this?

    a) Satan
    b) Jewish leaders
    c) His disciples
    d) those who came to the garden to arrest Him

7. Paul taught the Corinthians that three things are unending. Charity, or love, is the greatest of them. What are the other two?

8. The apostle John said perfect love casts out _____ .

    a) hatred
    b) fear
    c) jealousy
    d) Satan

9. The apostle John said we should not love "in word, neither in tongue" but _____ .

    a) in deed and in truth
    b) in humility and in awe
    c) in honesty and with whole heart
    d) in every act and every breath

10. Who said Christians should show godly love for one another with a holy kiss of greeting?

    a) Jesus
    b) John
    c) Paul
    d) Peter

Mortals' Miracles

1. Who wielded a rod at the Lord's bidding and thereby turned Egypt's waters to blood?

    a) Moses
    b) Aaron
    c) Caleb
    d) Joshua

2. After the plague of frogs, the Lord empowered Moses and Aaron to produce this affliction in Egypt.

    a) ants
    b) snakes
    c) cancer
    d) lice

3. At Joshua's request, what did God do to the sun in order to help the Israelites slay the Amorites?

    a) made it rise three hours earlier than normal
    b) eclipsed it
    c) made it shine hot enough to set the Amorites' leather battle dress aflame
    d) made it stand still for a whole day

4. What two Old Testament men of God brought corpses to life?

5. God empowered Elisha to part the River Jordan with _____ .

    a) a wave of his hand
    b) a nod of his head
    c) Elijah's cloak
    d) two palm leaves

6. Jesus told His disciples they could perform miracles even more powerful than His own. But to do it, they would need _____ .

    a) faith
    b) pure hearts
    c) God's inspiration
    d) guidance by the Holy Spirit

7. After Christ's ascension, what was the first recorded miracle performed by His disciples?

    a) Peter healing a blind woman
    b) Peter healing a crippled man
    c) John's inexplicable escape from Roman pursuers
    d) John's inexplicable escape from Jewish leaders

8. True or False: Stephen was noted for the miracles he performed before his martyrdom.

9. Who was the man Peter cured of palsy?

    a) Cornelius
    b) Philemon
    c) Aeneas
    d) Malchus

10. Who was the woman Peter raised from the dead?

    a) Lydia
    b) Dorcas
    c) Ginger
    d) Mariah

Mountains

1. On what mountain range did Noah's ark come to rest?

    a) Alp
    b) Appennine
    c) Ararat
    d) Carpathia

2. To what mountain did Abraham go to sacrifice Isaac?

    a) Horeb
    b) Moriah
    c) Hermon
    d) Pisgah

3. On what mountain did God speak to Moses from a burning bush?

    a) Olivet
    b) Sinai
    c) Hermon
    d) Horeb

4. On what mountain did God give Moses the Ten Commandments on stone tablets?

5. Aaron died atop this mountain.

    a) Olivet
    b) Hor
    c) Hermon
    d) Sinai

6. It was from the top of this mountain that God showed Moses the promised land.

    a) Sinai
    b) Olivet
    c) Carmel
    d) Pisgah

7. Mount Carmel was the scene of what great confrontation?

    a) the Israelites vs. the Philistines
    b) the Israelites vs. the Assyrians
    c) Absalom's army vs. David's army
    d) Elijah vs. the false prophets

8. Mount Sion also was called Mount _____ .

    a) Ararat
    b) Sinai
    c) Cardiff
    d) Hermon

9. King David fled to this mountain during Absalom's uprising.

   a) Carpathia
   b) Olivet
   c) Hermon
   d) Sinai

10. Matthew records Jesus giving His disciples the Great Commission on what mountain?

   a) Olivet
   b) Horeb
   c) Pisgah
   d) not named

Music

1. True or False: Miriam, sister of Moses and Aaron, was one of the first music and dance leaders noted in the Bible.

2. With what musical instruments were seven priests ordered to lead the Israelites against Jericho?

   a) brass trumpets
   b) reed flutes
   c) ox horns
   d) none of the above

3. A musical, prophetic frenzy caused this Old Testament person, filled with the Holy Spirit, to be "turned into another man."

   a) Aaron
   b) Samuel
   c) David
   d) Saul

4. Whose harp playing gave King Saul soothing respite from evil spirits?

   a) Jonathan's
   b) David's
   c) Michal's
   d) Micah's

5. 2 Chronicles names the _____ as temple singers.
   a) Benjamites
   b) Jebusites
   c) Levites
   d) Horebites

6. King Nebuchadnezzar used music as a signal for what?
   a) for the Feast of the Passover to begin
   b) for his army to attack the Israelites
   c) for his subjects to bow and worship his golden image
   d) for his mother's entrance into his throne room

7. True or False: Jesus and His disciples sang at the Last Supper.

8. Paul asserted that unless he displayed charity in his life, all his fine words bore no more meaning than these two musical instruments.
   a) harp and cymbal
   b) brass and cymbal
   c) harp and flute
   d) brass and flute

9. True or False: The apostle Paul encouraged the church to use music in worship.

10. What musical instrument does each of the seven angels hold at the opening of the seventh seal in Revelation?
    a) triangle
    b) ram's horn
    c) goat's horn
    d) trumpet

Obedience to God

1. Counting Noah, how many people obeyed God's commands, boarded the ark, and survived the flood?

2. The first altar to God recorded in the Bible was built by _____.
   a) Adam
   b) Noah
   c) Abraham
   d) Jacob

3. Because Lot's wife disobeyed the angel's instructions in fleeing Sodom and looked back, what happened to her?

    a) she was killed in the rain of fire and brimstone
    b) she was struck dumb
    c) she was blinded by the explosions
    d) she turned to salt

4. The famous human offering, agonizingly tied to an altar by his obedient father because God commanded it, was _____ .

    a) Abel
    b) Isaac
    c) Jacob
    d) Samuel

5. By God's instructions, when the Israelites offered sacrifices, they were to:

    a) sacrifice defective livestock or grain, trusting God to make it perfect
    b) sacrifice swine as a token of giving up their sinful ways
    c) sacrifice their best products, carefully chosen and prepared
    d) never defile a sacrifice with olive oil

6. According to Samuel, obedience to the Lord is better than

    _____ .

7. This son diverted the Israelites' obedience from his father.

    a) Simeon
    b) Absalom
    c) Zedekiah
    d) Jezebel

8. What turned the aging Solomon from the path of obedience to one of idolatry?

    a) wealth
    b) paranoia
    c) his wives
    d) his children

9. When Daniel as a youth was brought to Nebuchadnezzar's court, he kept himself clean according to Old Testament law by:

    a) singing a psalm of David before every meal
    b) refusing to eat unleavened bread
    c) refusing to drink water from the Babylonian pool
    d) refusing to dine on royal meat and wine

10. The first martyr known to have died for his devotion to Christ was _____ .
    a) Andrew
    b) Luke
    c) Matthias
    d) Stephen

Occupations in the Old Testament

1. Who was the first shepherd described in the Bible?

2. Shamgar, who slew 600 Philistines with an ox goad, was a _____ .
    a) blacksmith
    b) drover
    c) judge
    d) army commander under King David

3. An exceptional Old Testament hunter was _____ .
    a) David
    b) Jonathan
    c) Nimrod
    d) Joshua

4. What was Deborah besides a prophetess?

5. King David's earliest known occupation was _____ .
    a) shepherd
    b) carpenter
    c) court musician
    d) assistant to an astronomer

6. True or False: King David was a poet.

7. Before leading the Jews in rebuilding Jerusalem, what were Ezra and Nehemiah by profession, respectively?
    a) cloth merchant and court musician
    b) cheese merchant and stable tender
    c) Jewish teacher and king's wine steward
    d) slave overseer and carpenter

8. The prophet Daniel was a _____ .

    a) net maker
    b) teacher/slave in King Nebuchadnezzar's court
    c) royal accountant
    d) soldier

9. The prophet Amos was a _____ .

    a) shepherd
    b) carpenter
    c) potter
    d) goat merchant

10. Job was a _____ .

    a) judge
    b) livestock owner
    c) vintner
    d) court chef

Occupations in the New Testament

1. What was Zacharias, John the Baptist's father?

    a) priest
    b) tax collector
    d) doctor
    c) farmer

2. The apostle Andrew was a _____ .

    a) carpenter who worked with Jesus and Joseph
    b) sexton at the temple in Jerusalem
    c) fisherman in the Sea of Galilee
    d) sailmaker on the Mediterranean coast

3. The apostle Luke was a _____ .

    a) fisherman
    b) carpenter
    c) tax collector
    d) doctor

4. Nicodemus was a _____ .

    a) map maker
    b) religious leader
    c) tax collector
    d) tailor

5. Bartimaeus was a _____ .

    a) Jewish high priest
    b) beggar
    c) cloth merchant
    d) herdsman

6. Zacchaeus was a _____ .

    a) map maker
    b) religious leader
    c) tax collector
    d) tailor

7. Cornelius was a _____ .

    a) fisherman
    b) map maker
    c) centurion
    d) Roman governor

8. Lydia of Thyatira was a _____ .

    a) servant in the house of a Roman guard
    b) wealthy widow
    c) weaver of reed baskets
    d) cloth seller

9. Paul and Acquila both were _____ by trade.

    a) sail makers
    b) tent makers
    c) net makers
    d) candle makers

10. Paul's teaching deflated the livelihoods of the idol manufacturers in _____ .

    a) Ephesus
    b) Rhodes
    c) Philippi
    d) Crete

Parents and Children
I

1. Abraham and Hagar, Sarah's servant, had a son named
   _____ .

   a) Isaac
   b) Ishmael
   c) Ward
   d) Abner

2. Which was not a child of Abraham and Keturah?

   a) Jokshan
   b) Midian
   c) Isaac
   d) Ishbak

3. Who was the mother of Joseph and Benjamin?

   a) Sarah
   b) Rachel
   c) Rebecca
   d) Anna

4. Unable to bear children, Hannah promised God that if He would allow her to have a son, she would commit the child to a life of service to God. Thus was born _____ .

   a) Eli
   b) Samuel
   c) Saul
   d) Elkanah

5. The sons of Eli

   a) became the judges of Israel
   b) became the priests of Israel
   c) became the prophets of Israel
   d) became ungodly men

6. Who was King David's father?

   a) Eli
   b) Samuel
   c) Jesse
   d) Saul

7. How did King Saul's son Jonathan die?

    a) drowning
    b) killed by Philistines
    c) murdered by assassins hired by his brother Abinadab
    d) the Bible doesn't say

8. Who was Solomon's mother?

    a) Haggith
    b) Eglah
    c) Michal
    d) Bathsheba

9. The prophet Isaiah's father was _____ .

    a) Amoz
    b) Eli
    c) Ezra
    d) Solomon

10. What was the name of John the Baptist's mother?

Parents and Children
II

1. This man had three sons named Shem, Ham, and Japheth.

    a) Noah
    b) Joseph
    c) Dan
    d) Benjamin

2. "[W]ith thy blessing let the house of thy servant be blessed for ever." Thus concluded the lengthy prayer of this father for his family.

    a) Noah
    b) Abraham
    c) Jacob
    d) David

3. Who was Samuel's father?

    a) Elkanah
    b) Jeroham
    c) Elihu
    d) the Bible does not say

4. Who was King Saul's father?

   a) Samuel
   b) Kish
   c) Bichri
   d) Amasa

5. Who was the father of Michal, David's first wife?

   a) Nathan
   b) Abner
   c) Saul
   d) Ahimelech

6. Which son of Solomon "reigned in his stead" after Solomon's death?

   a) Jeroboam
   b) Rehoboam
   c) Nebat
   d) Asa

7. King Asa deposed Maachah as the queen mother because:

   a) she confronted him with his wickedness
   b) she refused to obey his edict concerning clothing
   c) she worshipped an idol
   d) he learned she was his aunt, not his mother

8. Good King Hezekiah had an evil father:

   a) Zechariah
   b) Menahem
   c) Pekahiah
   d) Ahaz

9. The prophet Hosea's father was _____ .

   a) Haman
   b) Beeri
   c) Pekah
   d) Shallum

10. Jesus from the cross commanded which disciple to take care of Jesus' mother Mary?

Parents and Children
III

1. Who was Noah's father?

    a) Adam
    b) Lamech
    c) Jared
    d) the Bible does not record

2. The Lord punished David by letting his infant son die of sickness. Who was the child's mother?

    a) Abigail
    b) Michal
    c) Bathsheba
    d) the Bible does not record

3. How many children did Solomon have?

    a) 88
    b) 700
    c) 7,000
    d) the Bible does not specify

4. When this man rebuilt Jericho, it cost him the lives of his oldest and youngest sons.

    a) Solomon
    b) Baasha
    c) Elah
    d) Hiel

5. During the siege of Samaria by King Benhadad, what did some of the beleaguered parents do with their children?

    a) offered them as living sacrifices to God
    b) killed them and offered their corpses as sacrifices to God
    c) killed them for food
    d) hid them in sacks of grain

6. God allowed Satan to kill how many of Job's children?

    a) three
    b) five
    c) six
    d) ten

7. This man's daughter, unwittingly sacrificed by her father's command, became the honoree of an Israelite celebration.

    a) Moses
    b) Aaron
    c) Jephtha
    d) David

8. Master craftsman Bezaleel was the son of _____ .

    a) Reuben
    b) Moses
    c) Uri
    d) Nehemiah

9. The prophet Hosea and his promiscuous wife Gomer had a daughter, _____ , whose name signified an end to God's mercy on Israel.

    a) Loruhama
    b) Naarah
    c) Hushim
    d) Shiphrah

10. Who was Timothy's mother?

    a) Lois
    b) Eunice
    c) Lydia
    d) Beverly

Patriarchs

1. How did Methuselah's father die?

    a) in the flood
    b) killed by Sodomites
    c) he didn't; God simply "took him"
    d) not reported in Scripture

2. The patriarch of the Jewish nation was _____ .

3. Who was the earthly father of the twelve tribes of Israel?

    a) Abraham
    b) Isaac
    c) Jacob
    d) Benjamin

4. Not included among the twelve tribes of Israel was that of
   _____ .

   a) Samuel
   b) Gad
   c) Asher
   d) Zebulun

5. Jacob instructed his sons to bury him in _____ .

   a) Syria
   b) Assyria
   c) Egypt
   d) Canaan

6. In what country did Jacob's son Joseph die?

7. Surprisingly, God once "sought to kill" this famous patriarch.

   a) Abram
   b) Joseph, son of Jacob
   c) Moses
   d) David

8. How did Samson die?

   a) by deliberately collapsing a temple on top of himself and
      his enemies
   b) by drowning
   c) by a spear thrust through his breast after the Philistines
      had cut his hair
   d) of old age

9. Before he departed the earth, Elijah the prophet offered to grant
   his successor Elisha one request. What did Elisha ask for?

   a) wisdom
   b) the power to foresee the future
   c) the power to heal
   d) a double portion of Elijah's spirit

10. To what early leader of His people did God offer a choice of three
    punishments for sin?

    a) Moses
    b) Joshua
    c) Saul
    d) David

Peoples of the Bible

1. Noah's ancient curse on these people was fulfilled when Joshua conquered their land and made them Israel's servants.

    a) descendants of Shem
    b) descendants of Canaan
    c) descendants of Japheth
    d) descendants of Cush

2. Rebekah and her brother Laban were members of this group.

    a) Syrians
    b) Mongolians
    c) Moabites
    d) Elamites

3. The sons of Jacob annihilated the males of these people because one of them, Shechem, defiled their sister Dinah.

    a) Canaanites
    b) Hivites
    c) Perizzites
    d) Jebusites

4. To what group of merchants did Joseph's brothers sell him into slavery?

    a) Egyptians
    b) Ishmaelites
    c) Edomites
    d) Horites

5. Moses' spies in Canaan reported this notable detail about the Anakites.

    a) they wore no clothes
    b) all the men were one-eyed
    c) they were giants
    d) they were dwarfs

6. Balak, the king who abhorred Balaam's prophesy, ruled what people?

    a) Benjamites
    b) Ishmaelites
    c) Israelites
    d) Moabites

7. Delilah, Samson's betrayer, belonged to what group of people?

    a) Benjamites
    b) Ammonites
    c) Amalekites
    d) Philistines

8. Benhadad was a king of the _____ .

    a) Philistines
    b) Mesopotamians
    c) Syrians
    d) Macedonians

9. Baladan was one of the kings of these once-powerful people.

    a) Mesopotamians
    b) Babylonians
    c) Ammonites
    d) Moabites

10. These people killed some of Job's servants.

    a) Sabeans
    b) Philistines
    c) Amalekites
    d) all of the above

Persecution and Martyrdom

1. Why didn't the Egyptians want Pharaoh to let the Israelites leave?

    a) they were using the Israelites as slaves
    b) they were afraid the Israelites would organize an army and come back to invade Egypt
    c) they believed God would protect Egypt as long as the Israelites were around
    d) none of the above

2. Obadiah hid a hundred prophets in a cave to escape the rampage of whom?

    a) the Philistines
    b) Saul
    c) Ahab
    d) Jezebel

3. When Job's children were killed in a windstorm, what was Job's response?

    a) he killed himself
    b) he raged at God
    c) he worshipped God
    d) he worshipped alien gods

4. Who was the second follower of Christ reported to have been killed for his faith?

    a) Stephen
    b) Peter
    c) Thaddeus
    d) James

5. In the Sermon on the Mount, what did Jesus say your response should be when people "despitefully use you, and persecute you?"

    a) ignore them
    b) turn the other cheek
    c) pray for them
    d) speak to them privately; if they won't stop, speak to them with two witnesses, then take your case before the church elders

6. The logical argument of this Pharisee resulted in the release from prison of Peter and other apostles (though not without a whipping).

    a) Gamaliel
    b) Hillel
    c) Dodus
    d) Narcissus

7. As recorded in Acts, how did James the brother of John die?

    a) by the rope
    b) by the sword
    c) by fire at the stake
    d) by crucifixion

8. What was the response of the Jews to James' death?

    a) they were pleased
    b) they were afraid because they saw in it the fulfillment of prophetic condemnation
    c) they were afraid because they feared it was the beginning of a period of genocide
    d) none; Herod had James slain in secret

9. When Stephen was stoned, who minded his tormenters' cloaks?

10. Who cried "Lord, lay not this sin to their charge" at the moment of death?

    a) John the Baptist
    b) Jesus Christ
    c) Stephen
    d) Paul

Plagues and Afflictions

1. What was Moses' notable deficiency?

    a) absence of his right leg below the knee
    b) absence of his right forefinger
    c) speech impediment
    d) near blindness

2. Moses is the first person the Bible reports to have been cured of _____ .

    a) blindness
    b) speech impediment
    c) boils
    d) leprosy

3. The Lord punished Moses' sister Miriam with a physical affliction because she questioned Moses' unique relationship with God. What was her affliction?

    a) inability to speak for two years
    b) leprosy
    c) inability to conceive
    d) internal bleeding

4. After God sent poisonous snakes to plague the rebellious Israelites and they repented, He gave them this snakebite remedy.

    a) a bronze snake on a pole
    b) a healing spring
    c) a wild herb
    d) a potion of calf's blood, olive oil, and honey

5. Jonathan's son (Saul's grandson) Mephibosheth had a physical disability. What was it?

    a) he was blind
    b) he was missing an arm
    c) he was deaf
    d) he was lame

6. This king, "diseased in his feet," refused to seek the Lord's help and, relying solely on his royal physicians, died.

    a) Oded
    b) Asa
    c) Jehoshaphat
    d) Joash

7. How did King Ahaziah end up on what would become his deathbed?

    a) leprosy
    b) arrow wound
    c) falling through an upstairs lattice
    d) lung disease—probably pneumonia

8. In Jesus' time, where did afflicted Jews go because of its healing waters?

    a) Tyre
    b) the pool of Bethesda
    c) the River Jordan
    d) the Dead Sea

9. Who cured Saul/Paul of blindness?

    a) Ananias
    b) Luke
    c) Barnabas
    d) Lydia

10. Who prescribed prayerful anointment with oil to heal the sick?

    a) Aaron
    b) Jesus
    c) Luke
    d) James

Prayer

1. According to Genesis, people began to pray to God after this man's birth.

    a) Abel's
    b) Seth's
    c) Enos'
    d) Shem's

2. What patriarch prayed fervently for God to spare a sinful city?

    a) Noah
    b) Abraham
    c) Moses
    d) Joshua

3. Shortly before the parting and crossing of the Red Sea, God rebuked Moses for praying. Why?

    a) because Moses had not secluded himself
    b) because Moses had not taken time to adopt a reverent attitude
    c) because Moses had forgotten to offer a sacrifice
    d) because Moses was stalling when he should have been taking action

4. Which Psalm is David's prayer for forgiveness after his adultery with Bathsheba?

    a) 4
    b) 14
    c) 41
    d) 51

5. One of God's best-known responses to prayer is: "If my people, which are called by my name, shall humble themselves, and pray, and seek my face, and turn from their wicked ways; then will I hear from heaven, and will forgive their sin, and will heal their land." To whom did God make this pledge?

   a) Abraham
   b) Moses
   c) Solomon
   d) Jeremiah

6. What was the occasion for that promise?

   a) internal strife among God's people
   b) famine
   c) foreign captivity
   d) dedication of the temple in Jerusalem

7. Jesus taught that when we pray, we shouldn't use "_____ as the heathen do."

   a) sophisticated words
   b) pious pleadings
   c) vain repetitions
   d) Roman pleasantries

8. In which two gospels do we find the Lord's Prayer?

9. How many times did Paul pray for God to take away his physical ailment?

   a) three
   b) eleven
   c) eighteen
   d) twenty-five

10. What was God's response to Paul's prayer for relief from his affliction?

   a) This is the cross I have given thee to bear
   b) But nine years, and this shall be granted unto thee
   c) This is thy joy
   d) My grace is sufficient for thee

Prophets and Prophesies
I

1. According to the prophet Habakkuk, the horses of the fierce Chaldean army were _____ .

    a) as large as elephants
    b) as black as night
    c) fire breathers
    d) swifter than leopards

2. Which Old Testament prophet specified that Bethlehem would be Jesus' birthplace?

    a) Jeremiah
    b) Daniel
    c) Hosea
    d) Micah

3. Which Old Testament prophet foretold the virgin birth?

    a) Isaiah
    b) Jeremiah
    c) Jonah
    d) Joel

4. The prophet in the watchtower was _____ .

    a) Ezekiel
    b) Habakkuk
    c) Amos
    d) Nahum

5. "Babylon is fallen!" was part of a vision of _____ .

    a) Isaiah
    b) Obadiah
    c) Amos
    d) Micah

6. The prophet who had a promiscuous wife was _____ .

    a) Hosea
    b) Job
    c) Daniel
    d) Mordecai

7. God commanded that prophet to:

    a) have his wife condemned to death
    b) love his wife
    c) renew the marriage ceremony between him and his wife
    d) divorce his wife

8. What is one facet of the Gospel the prophet Zechariah foresaw?

    a) the virgin birth
    b) Christ's birth in Bethlehem
    c) Christ's entry into Jerusalem on a donkey
    d) the rending of the temple veil at Christ's death

9. John the Baptist baptized with water. Jesus, he told the people, would come to baptize with the Holy Ghost and with _____ .

10. The so-called "four horsemen of the apocalypse" are described in the book of _____ .

    a) Joshua
    b) 2 Kings
    c) 2 Kings
    d) Revelation

Prophets and Prophesies
II

1. How many false prophets did Elisha challenge in the famous encounter on Mount Carmel?

    a) 400
    b) 450
    c) 800
    d) 850

2. Elijah and Elisha were startled by the appearance of a heavenly horse and chariot made of _____ .

    a) gold
    b) silver
    c) emeralds
    d) fire

3. Psalm 22 correctly predicted what detail of the earthly life of Christ?

    a) that He would be born of a virgin
    b) that He would walk on water
    c) that He would make blind people see
    d) that mockers would gamble for His clothes beneath the cross

4. This prophet was branded a traitor by his own people and cast into a dungeon, where he literally "sunk in the mire."

    a) Jeremiah
    b) Joel
    c) Jonah
    d) Micah

5. Amos told the Israelites their sins would be punished by a devastating famine; the Lord would take away _____ .

    a) their bread
    b) their wine
    c) their water
    d) His Word

6. Through this prophet, God promised to make Judah's governor, Zerubbabel, "as a signet."

    a) Jeremiah
    b) Daniel
    c) Haggai
    d) Malachi

7. In addition to Daniel and Ezekiel, which Old Testament prophet spoke of the end times?

    a) Hosea
    b) Micah
    c) Nahum
    d) Zechariah

8. This prophet saw a man preparing to measure Jerusalem.

    a) Isaiah
    b) Jeremiah
    c) Jonah
    d) Zechariah

9. Which angel did God send to Zacharias to announce the coming pregnancy of his wife Elisabeth and birth of John the Baptist?

 a) Michael
 b) Gabriel
 c) Gideon
 d) Samuel

10. Which angel did God send to the Virgin Mary to reveal His plan for Jesus' birth?

 a) Michael
 b) Gabriel
 c) Gideon
 d) Samuel

Prophets and Prophesies
III

1. Before joining Elijah, what kind of work did Elisha do?

 a) fortune telling
 b) fishing
 c) herding
 d) farming

2. At Gilgal, the prophet Elisha performed what miracle similar to one of Jesus' own?

 a) caused evil spirits to leave a human and enter a herd of swine
 b) turned water into wine
 c) fed a lot of people with a little bread
 d) ascended into heaven

3. Which prophet predicted the earth would "reel to and fro like a drunkard"?

 a) Isaiah
 b) Ezekiel
 c) Hosea
 d) Joel

4. Who predicted correctly that King Cyrus would order the rebuilding of the temple in Jerusalem?

    a) Elisha
    b) Isaiah
    c) Daniel
    d) Haggai

5. Which prophet prophesied of Jesus as "despised and rejected of men; a man of sorrows, and acquainted with grief"?

    a) Isaiah
    b) Jeremiah
    c) Ezekiel
    d) Amos

6. Jeremiah prophesied that at the wrath of God, the earth will:

    a) turn dark
    b) burn
    c) crack open
    d) tremble

7. Who prophesied against Edom?

    a) Jeremiah
    b) Amos
    c) Obadiah
    d) Zephaniah

8. This prophet warned the city of Nineveh it would be overthrown in forty days.

    a) Daniel
    b) Jonah
    c) Micah
    d) Habakkuk

9. What did the king of Nineveh do in response to that prophet's warning?

    a) sat in ashes and repented
    b) had the prophet beheaded
    c) had the prophet drowned
    d) declared war against Judah and was killed

10. "[S]mite the shepherd, and the sheep shall be scattered." What Old Testament prophet made that statement, which was cited by Jesus on the Mount of Olives concerning His disciples?

    a) Isaiah
    b) Ezekiel
    c) Joel
    d) Zechariah

Revelation

1. Revelation was written to _____ .

    a) the seven churches of Asia
    b) the Nazarenes
    c) the Romans
    d) the Athenians

2. God's two witnesses during the end times will prophesy in sackcloth for how long?

    a) 14 months
    b) 31 days
    c) 1,260 days
    d) 11 weeks

3. In John's vision, which archangel leads God's forces in casting Satan from Heaven?

    a) Gideon
    b) Aniam
    c) Michael
    d) Daniel

4. During that celestial battle, Satan is in the form of a _____ .

    a) snake
    b) dragon
    c) four-headed bear
    d) six-headed bear

5. This dreaded number is the mark of the beast.

    a) 13
    b) 99
    c) 666
    d) 999

6. "And the smoke of their torment ascendeth up for ever and ever: and they have no rest day or night . . ." John prophesied this about _____ .

    a) the scribes and Pharisees
    b) backsliders
    c) descendants of the ancient Ammonites
    d) those who receive the mark of the beast

7. The final earthly battle before Jesus' return will be fought at _____ .

8. John saw an angel descend from heaven and cast Satan into the bottomless pit for how many years?

    a) 3 years
    b) 7 years
    c) 1,000 years
    d) forever

9. After Satan's defeat, John says there will be a new heaven, a new earth, and no more _____ .

    a) horizon
    b) sea
    c) sky
    d) sun

10. The new kingdom will be graced with a river of water flowing from God's throne, as clear as _____ .

    a) glass
    b) the air
    c) diamond
    d) crystal

Riches

1. Joseph went from imprisonment to a position of power and wealth by interpreting Pharaoh's dream. What specific rewards did Pharaoh immediately lavish upon him?

    a) Pharaoh's own ring
    b) elegant clothes
    c) a gold necklace
    d) all of the above

2. The Lord touched the minds of the Egyptians so that they gave these riches to the departing Israelites.

    a) silver and frankincense
    b) silver and gold
    c) silver, gold, and cloth
    d) gold, frankincense, and livestock

3. The prophet Amos chastised the luxurious lifestyles of Israelites who slept on beds made of _____ .

    a) sandalwood
    b) ivory
    c) ebony
    d) copper plating

4. How many talents of gold did King Solomon amass in one year?

    a) 11
    b) 12
    c) 666
    d) 1,200

5. Proverbs 8 says wisdom is far more valuable than what gem?

6. Proverbs 22 says "_____ is rather to be chosen than great riches."

7. Jesus explained in the Sermon on the Mount that you should "store your treasures in heaven" because if you collect earthly treasures, they will be subject to moth, rust, and _____.

    a) misplacement
    b) fire
    c) thieves
    d) worms

8. Jesus went on to say in the famous sermon that people tend to invest their _____ where they invest their treasures.

9. Later in the Sermon on the Mount, He decried the foolishness of throwing "_____ before swine" to be trampled.

    a) gold
    b) silver
    c) rubies
    d) pearls

10. What became of Judas' tainted thirty pieces of silver?

　　a) the priests divided the money privately
　　b) they were used to buy a graveyard for strangers
　　c) they went into the temple fund set aside for paupers
　　d) Pilate confiscated the money

Servants

1. What Old Testament relatives had servants who squabbled over grazing rights, prompting their masters to separate?

　　a) the sons of Noah
　　b) Abraham and Lot
　　c) Esau and Jacob
　　d) the sons of Jacob

2. In Deuteronomy, the Lord warned His people through Moses that if they disobeyed, he would send them by ship as bondservants to _____ .

　　a) Tyre
　　b) Crete
　　c) Egypt
　　d) Pamphylia

3. This man refused to provide food and drink for David, suspecting David and his men might be runaway servants.

　　a) Abiathar
　　b) Nabal
　　c) Doeg
　　d) Ahitub

4. This cunning servant apparently got much more than he deserved by scheming to outwit King David and Jonathan's son Mephibosheth.

　　a) Ziba
　　b) Telah
　　c) Elihoreph
　　d) Zethan

5. Elisha had a greedy servant named _____ .

　　a) Oman
　　b) Ritsi
　　c) Oj
　　d) Gehazi

6. What king freed his captive servants to return to their homeland as builders?

    a) Solomon
    b) Jehoahaz
    c) Zedekiah
    d) Cyrus

7. Queen Esther's chamberlain/messenger was _____ .

    a) Hamedatha
    b) Mordecai
    c) Hatach
    d) Haman

8. Jesus from a distance healed the servant of a believing centurion. What was the servant's problem?

    a) palsy
    b) leprosy
    c) deafness
    d) stab wound

9. What startling act of servitude by Jesus initially was rejected by Peter?

10. Paul from prison wrote to Philemon on behalf of this servant.

    a) Titus
    b) Onesimus
    c) Cornelius
    d) Timothy

Signs and Omens
I

1. After sending a dove from the ark the third time, Noah knew the flood had receded enough to expose dry land because:

    a) the dove returned and signaled the news
    b) the dove's mate subsequently flew out to meet the dove
    c) the dove did not return to the ark
    d) the dove returned with a twig in its beak

2. God promised Noah He never again would destroy the earth with a flood. What sign did He show as a remembrance of this promise?

   a) creation of the River Jordan to always carry away His wrath
   b) creation of the Sea of Galilee to always contain His wrath
   c) creation of a red sky at dawn
   d) creation of a rainbow in the clouds

3. By what sign did Abraham's servant know Rebekah was chosen by the Lord to be Isaac's wife?

4. What was it about the famous burning bush that attracted Moses' attention?

5. To make sure God wanted him to lead the Israelites in battle, Gideon asked the Lord to show him signs involving _____ .

   a) wool on a threshing floor
   b) a burning bush
   c) unseen trumpets sounding from a hilltop
   d) a river of blood

6. In the midst of a merry banquet, this Babylonian king froze in horror as mysterious handwriting appeared on the palace wall. Before the next sunrise, he was dead—just as the writing predicted. Who was the king?

   a) Nebuchadnezzar
   b) Belshazzar
   c) Darius
   d) the King of the North

7. The sign by which the shepherds would recognize the baby Jesus as Christ, an angel told them, would be _____ .

   a) the star of Bethlehem
   b) a halo
   c) a voice from a cloud
   d) the manger scene

8. Red sky in the morning means foul weather; red sky in the evening means fair weather. Who made this observation in Matthew 16?

   a) Matthew
   b) Peter
   c) the centurion
   d) Jesus

9. The signal by which Judas identified Jesus to the mob at Gethsemane was a _____ .

    a) waved lantern
    b) greeting with his upraised left hand
    c) kiss
    d) greeting with the words "Hail, Master!"

10. Immediately after Jesus died on the cross, which of the following did not occur?

    a) the temple veil was torn in half
    b) the earth shook
    c) a comet temporarily blinded the Roman executioners
    d) dead saints emerged from their tombs

Signs and Omens
II

1. As a sign commemorating their crossing of the dried-up Jordan, God commanded the Israelites to build _____ .

    a) the Ark of the Covenant
    b) a temple at Jericho
    c) a temple at Gilgal
    d) a monument of twelve stones

2. What did people do in Old Testament days as a sign of ownership?

    a) branded their property
    b) staked their claims before the priests at a temple ceremony
    c) gave away a shoe
    d) exchanged kisses

3. How did God help Gideon select his soldiers to defeat the Midianites?

    a) by their lineage
    b) by the way they drank water
    c) by their clothing
    d) by their response to a greeting

4. The dying Elisha foretold a triple defeat of Syria by this sign.

   a) the shooting of arrows
   b) a cock crowing three times
   c) the passage of three days between his prophesy and his death
   d) the movement of a sundial shadow

5. To affirm His promise that gravely ill King Hezekiah would live and reign fifteen more years, God showed him this sign.

   a) He set back the shadow of a sundial
   b) He suddenly turned Hezekiah's fever to an icy chill
   c) He split the stone exterior wall of the king's bed chamber
   d) He momentarily transfigured the body of Hezekiah's adviser Isaiah into a blinding light

6. Which prophet went naked for three years as a warning to Egypt and Ethiopia?

   a) Elijah
   b) Isaiah
   c) Ezekiel
   d) Hosea

7. When Jesus sent His disciples out to preach, what symbolic act did He tell them to perform as they departed unwelcoming cities?

   a) publicly denouncing the local temple priest
   b) publicly washing the feet of the local temple priest
   c) refusing to pay alms to beggars at the city gate
   d) shaking the dust from their feet

8. Jesus said "an evil and adulterous generation" would be given only "the sign of the prophet Jonas." To what was he referring?

   a) Jonah's refusal to obey God, and the subsequent punishment
   b) Jonah's willingness to let himself be cast overboard into the stormy sea
   c) Jonah's three days inside the fish, symbolic of Jesus' pending three days of death
   d) Jonah's warning that Nineveh would be destroyed in forty days

9. Jesus showed the apostle John this clear signal identifying His future betrayer.

   a) a kiss
   b) a washing of the betrayer's feet
   c) a silver cup
   d) a piece of bread

10. By what sign does the angel mark the 144,000 servants of God in the seventh chapter of Revelation?

    a) a seal on the forehead
    b) a tattoo on the back of the hand
    c) entering their names in the Book of Life
    d) wings

Sins and Sinners

1. How did God destroy Sodom and Gomorrah?

    a) brimstone and fire rained from heaven
    b) fire caused by internal rioting
    c) pumpkin-size hail
    d) earthquake

2. The story of the angels' encounter with wicked men in Sodom is told in Genesis 19. In Judges 19, we read an uncannily similar account of a drama that occurred at _____ .

    a) Gomorrah
    b) Gilgal
    c) Gaza
    d) Gibeah

3. What infamous golden idol did Aaron create?

    a) horse
    b) calf
    c) pig
    d) lamb

4. King David's firstborn and heir apparent, this young man fell victim to his own lust.

    a) Amnon
    b) Chileab
    c) Absalom
    d) Shephatiah

5. After King David conspired to have Uriah killed in battle so he could have Uriah's wife Bathsheba, who confronted David with his sin?

    a) Joab
    b) Nathan
    c) Bathsheba
    d) Samuel

6. In order to obtain a prize vineyard for her husband King Ahab, Jezebel had this landowner stoned to death on a pretense.

   a) Benhadad
   b) Zophar
   c) Tobiah
   d) Naboth

7. "Thy first father hath sinned, and thy teachers have transgressed against, me." God convicted the Israelites of this through which prophet?

   a) Elijah
   b) Elisha
   c) Isaiah
   d) Malachi

8. John the Baptist chastised Herod for marrying _____.

   a) his brother's wife
   b) his own sister
   c) his own first cousin
   d) the wife of a Roman officer Herod had sent into exile

9. This person's exotic dancing caused King Herod to have John the Baptist beheaded.

   a) Herod's wife
   b) Herod's sister
   c) Herod's niece
   d) Herod's army commander's wife

10. For a particular sin, Paul told the Corinthians to "deliver such an one unto Satan for the destruction of the flesh," in hopes that the person's spirit would be saved on Judgment Day. What was the sin?

    a) first-degree murder
    b) any form of murder
    c) adultery with the sinner's mother-in-law
    d) taking the Lord's name in vain

Sleep

1. Fleeing to his Uncle Laban's after stealing his brother's blessing, Jacob fell asleep along the way. What did he use for a pillow?

2. How did Old Testament law help ensure that poor people got a good night's sleep?

   a) by requiring rich people to put them up for the night
   b) by requiring innkeepers to find them places to sleep in stables
   c) by requiring the maintenance of a poor house in each town
   d) by requiring lenders to return to them each night cloaks that were offered as collateral for loans

3. "Behold, thou shalt sleep with thy fathers; and this people will rise up, and go a whoring after the gods of the strangers of the land . . ." Whose impending death did God foretell in this way?

   a) Adam and Eve's
   b) Abraham's
   c) Jacob's
   d) Moses'

4. Who lost his hair by falling asleep?

5. The psalmist wrote that God gives sleep to _____ .

   a) hard workers
   b) the aged and infirm
   c) His beloved people
   d) weary warriors

6. In Ecclesiastes, we're told laborers enjoy their sleep. The rich, meanwhile, go sleepless because:

   a) God is displeased with them
   b) their riches consume their thoughts
   c) they're addicted to exhausting vices
   d) they feel guilty

7. "The damsel is not dead, but sleepeth," Jesus said before performing one of His most astonishing miracles. What did Jesus command upon the girl's rising?

   a) that her father build a new temple
   b) that her father become a fisher of men
   c) that her parents take in the hungry
   d) that no one be told, and that she be given something to eat

8. While Jesus' disciples slept in the Garden of Gethsemane, what was Jesus doing?

    a) also sleeping
    b) writing His will
    c) praying
    d) healing the sick

9. What was Jesus' comment when He found the disciples sleeping in the garden?

    a) "The Son of man is betrayed to be crucified."
    b) "For this people's heart is waxed gross, and their ears are dull of hearing, and their eyes they have closed."
    c) "But blessed are your eyes, for they see; and your ears, for they hear."
    d) "The spirit indeed is willing, but the flesh is weak."

10. Besides Jesus, what other biblical man once slept at sea, oblivious to a storm?

    a) Joshua
    b) Elijah
    c) Jonah
    d) Peter

Soldiers and Warfare
I

1. God told the Israelites that whenever He delivered a city belonging to certain enemies into their conquering hands, they must destroy every living thing within it. Which of the following were not among these specified mortal enemies?

    a) Amorites
    b) Philistines
    c) Perizzites
    d) Jebusites

2. How did Abimelech, Gideon's scheming son, die in battle?

    a) his half-brother Jotham wounded him with a poisoned arrow
    b) a woman of Thebez during a siege hit him in the head with a millstone
    c) he suffered a heart attack while laying siege to the tower of Shechem
    d) none of the above

3. When King Saul dressed David in the king's own armor before the confrontation with Goliath, David cast it off. What reason did David give?

    a) deception—he didn't want Goliath to think he was a warrior
    b) the armor was too cumbersome for him
    c) he wasn't worthy of wearing the king's armor
    d) the Lord had told him no armor would be necessary

4. True or False: David felled Goliath with a single stone from his sling.

5. Besides his sling, David used another weapon against Goliath. What was it?

    a) bow and arrow
    b) sword
    c) dagger
    d) poisonous serpent

6. This warrior became a bitter rival of Joab, David's army commander.

    a) Jonathan
    b) Azariah
    c) Abner
    d) Uzziah

7. Who killed King Saul?

    a) Philistine cavalrymen
    b) Philistine archers
    c) his own armor bearer
    d) he killed himself

8. What was done with King Saul's body after his death?

    a) it was mummified
    b) it was hung on a wall, then cremated
    c) it was cast into the sea
    d) it was entombed in a secret cave

9. One of the fiercest soldiers in the Old Testament histories was this nephew of King David, who killed 300 adversaries with his spear.

    a) Abinadab
    b) Adonijah
    c) Abishai
    d) Abner

10. During the Syrian siege of Samaria, the food shortage was so severe that the Israelites were reduced to eating _____ .

    a) donkeys' heads and doves' dung
    b) shoe leather
    c) the eyes of domestic animals
    d) the flesh of human dead

Soldiers and Warfare
II

1. It took more than trumpet blasts to bring down the walls of Jericho. What else did God command the Israelites to do?

    a) set fire to the walls with flaming arrows
    b) set fire to the walls with buckets of burning tar
    c) shout
    d) whistle

2. At one point while battling the Philistines, King Saul forbade his soldiers from eating anything until evening. Which of his soldiers unknowingly violated the command?

    a) Saul's son Jonathan
    b) David
    c) all David's older brothers
    d) Doeg the Edomite

3. Before David confronted him, Goliath offered a deal to the Israelite army. What were his terms?

    a) a 60/40 division of disputed territory, with no further fighting
    b) a 70/30 division of disputed territory, with no further fighting
    c) Goliath would fight the best Israelite soldier; the winner's army would subjugate the other, with no further fighting
    d) Goliath would fight the six best Israelites at once, winner take all

4. For sheltering and feeding fugitive David, Ahimelech and more than eighty other priests of Nob were executed by this mercenary for King Saul.

    a) Doeg
    b) Nadab
    c) Micaiah
    d) Joshibiah

5. How did Ahithophel, an important conspirator in Absalom's rebellion against King David, die?

    a) stabbed by Absalom, who distrusted him
    b) rode his donkey over a cliff
    c) drank poison
    d) hanged himself

6. This great warrior in King David's army slew "two lionlike men of Moab" and "a lion in the midst of a pit in time of snow."

    a) Asahel
    b) Joab
    c) Benaiah
    d) Shammah

7. Goliath had a giant brother "whose spear staff was like a weaver's beam." This warrior, killed in battle by Elhanan, was named _____ .

    a) Jair
    b) Lahmi
    c) Hadarezer
    d) Shophach

8. During the reign of good King Hezekiah, God preserved Israel by killing 185,000 of the enemy Assyrian army in a single night. How did He do it?

    a) with 140 select Israelite guerrilla fighters
    b) with 1,400 select Israelite guerrilla fighters
    c) with an angel
    d) with a ghastly plague, possibly spinal meningitis

9. King Solomon had how many horsemen?

    a) 1,000
    b) 12,000
    c) 40,000
    d) 400,000

10. During the latter years of King Asa's reign over Judah, his country was attacked by Baasha, king of what country?

    a) Philistia
    b) Syria
    c) Israel
    d) Babylon

Soldiers and Warfare
III

1. The wandering Israelites had a minimum draft age for their army. What was it, according to Numbers?

    a) fourteen
    b) eighteen
    c) twenty
    d) twenty-five

2. Old Testament law dismissed from military service any Israelite who:

    a) was an only son
    b) was engaged to be married
    c) had served four years already
    d) had fought in twelve battles already

3. Before sending them into battle against the Midianites, God reduced Gideon's army from 32,000 to what number?

    a) 8,000
    b) 6,000
    c) 300
    d) 100

4. Why did God radically shrink the size of Gideon's army?

    a) because their foes, the Midianites, were unfairly small in number
    b) to emphasize how weak the Midianites were
    c) to demonstrate that by using surprise, the Israelites could defeat any army, no matter what size
    d) because He knew that unless the victory was miraculous, the Israelites would credit themselves

5. When the Benjamites were conquered after their travesty at Gibeah, they fled to the rock of _____ .

    a) Sinai
    b) Rimmon
    c) Jericho
    d) ages

6. This valley proved to be a disastrous place for the Lord's Old Testament enemies to engage in battle.

    a) Valley of Blood
    b) Valley of Salt
    c) Valley of Death
    d) Valley of Sticks

7. When King Saul first went to war against the Philistines, his army was not equipped with swords or spears. Besides Saul himself, what other Israelite warrior had these?

    a) his son Jonathan
    b) David's father Jesse
    c) David's older brother Eliab
    d) Saul's armor bearer

8. When David appeared before him, the indignant Goliath cursed and vowed to _____ .

    a) quarter him and send the pieces to the four sides of the Sea of Galilee
    b) throw his flesh to wild animals
    c) send his head on a spear to King Saul
    d) send him back to King Saul alive, but with no fingers or toes

9. What season of year did Old Testament kings typically go to war?

    a) spring
    b) summer
    c) autumn
    d) winter

10. Which Psalm did King David write in exile during Absalom's coup?

    a) 1
    b) 3
    c) 59
    d) 95

Teachings

I

1. If you want to acquire wisdom, according to Psalm 111 and Proverbs 1, you first must have a _____ .
   - a) desire to learn
   - b) willingness to serve
   - c) godly fear
   - d) sound body

2. According to Proverbs 4, _____ is "the principal thing."
   - a) truth
   - b) wisdom
   - c) courage
   - d) birthright

3. Proverbs 15 teaches us to moderate our _____ in order to diffuse anger.
   - a) beverage consumption
   - b) speech
   - c) punishment of criminals
   - d) discipline of children

4. The final chapter of Proverbs contains the teachings of King Lemuel regarding _____ .
   - a) the virtuous woman
   - b) the slovenly man
   - c) the obedient daughter
   - d) the rebellious son

5. Scripture warns us that comforts and pleasures _____ .
   - a) are fleeting
   - b) lead to poverty
   - c) choke a person's understanding of God's word
   - d) all of the above

6. Jesus enraged listeners in His hometown Nazareth synagogue when he told them, among other things, that:
   - a) no prophet is welcome in his hometown
   - b) He had come to earth to reconcile the Nazarenes to God
   - c) He would die in Jerusalem, not Nazareth
   - d) none of the above

7. The Beatitudes are _____ .

    a) a sequence of warnings
    b) a sequence of commands
    c) a sequence of blessings
    d) a sequence of pardons

8. Don't worry—worry does nothing to lengthen your life. Who gave us this advice?

    a) Isaiah
    b) Amos
    c) Jesus
    d) Peter

9. In the Sermon on the Mount, Christ said that if you judge others, God will do this.

    a) judge you
    b) reward you
    c) honor you
    d) expect you to be able to explain your rationale on Judgment Day

10. In the eighth chapter of John, Jesus told His disciples the truth would make them _____ .

    a) blessed
    b) free
    c) wealthy
    d) wise

Teachings
II

1. Psalm 134 directs what specific group of people to praise the Lord?

    a) those in bondage
    b) the Israelite nation
    c) servants in the house of the Lord
    d) young people

2. Proverbs 28 teaches that it's foolish to trust in your own
_____ .

    a) ability
    b) wisdom
    c) heart
    d) strength

3. In the Beatitudes, Jesus said these people will obtain mercy.

    a) those who are poor
    b) those who are just
    c) those who are obedient
    d) those who are merciful

4. Jesus' warning about false prophets inspired the modern adage
about _____ .

    a) the pot calling the kettle black
    b) wolves in sheeps' clothing
    c) a stitch in time
    d) a bird in the hand

5. Speaking of His second coming, Jesus said it would be prefaced
by a time of "famines, and pestilences, and _____, in
divers places."

    a) floods
    b) burning cities
    c) earthquakes
    d) hail storms

6. In John's Gospel account, the famous "ask and it shall be given"
promise by Jesus is prefaced by a vital but often overlooked "if"
condition. What is the requirement?

7. In his letter to the Romans, Chapter 1, Paul explained that the
just shall live by _____ .

    a) perseverance
    b) faith
    c) works
    d) a peaceful river

8. The apostle Paul once likened Sarah's handmaid Hagar to
_____ .

    a) Babylon
    b) a martyr
    c) the Tower of Babel
    d) Mount Sinai

9. The apostle James warned that the tongue can be
   _____ .

10. The apostle John wrote that "he that _____ not
    knoweth not God."
    a) loveth
    b) repenteth
    c) prayeth
    d) none of the above

Teachings
III

1. The Lord hates seven things, according to the writer of Proverbs
   6. Name five of them.

2. Through Malachi, God told His people that by not tithing, they
   were _____ .
   a) assuring themselves of poverty
   b) assuring themselves of hellfire
   c) robbing Him
   d) dooming their children

3. Which specific teaching of Jesus Christ enraged the Jews to the
   extent that they tried to stone Him?
   a) that He had no earthly father
   b) that He existed before Abraham
   c) that He would destroy the temple and rebuild it in three
      days
   d) that they were hypocrites

4. Who instructed us in praying the Lord's Prayer?
   a) Paul
   b) Peter
   c) Matthew
   d) Jesus

5. What did Jesus teach us about marriage in heaven?

    a) that we'll be married to our earthly spouses
    b) that if we have more than one spouse, we'll be married to our first
    c) that there will be no marriages in heaven
    d) He didn't speak of marriage in heaven

6. Where is Jesus referred to as "Alpha and Omega, the beginning and the end"?

    a) His baptism
    b) the Last Supper
    c) His ascension into heaven
    d) the end of the world

7. Quoting from the prophet Joel, which apostle in the second chapter of Acts explained to skeptics the spirit-filled behavior of his companions on the day of Pentecost?

    a) Mark
    b) Peter
    c) Andrew
    d) Matthias

8. Paul instructed us to offer our _____ as living sacrifices.

    a) hearts
    b) families
    c) bodies
    d) possessions

9. The apostle Paul wrote how many published letters to the Corinthians?

10. Jesus taught that in order to save your life, what must you do?

Tongues to Speak

1. True or False: After the flood, Noah's descendants all spoke the same language.

2. In advising Job, Zophar observed that the wickedness hidden under the tongues of evil people tastes _____ .

    a) sweet
    b) bitter
    c) like salt
    d) like wine

3. The writer of Psalm 15 said "he that backbiteth . . . with his tongue" will be prohibited from _____ .

    a) serving as a high priest
    b) taking the sacrament of holy communion
    c) reading the Scriptures publicly
    d) entering God's holy tabernacle

4. The Proverbs say "a word fitly spoken" is comparable to _____ .

    a) "a stitch in time"
    b) "apples of gold in pictures of silver"
    c) "honey to the palate"
    d) "a dam to a flood"

5. When Peter exhorted that the godly man should "refrain his tongue from evil, and his lips that they speak no guile" (1 Peter 3:10), from what Old Testament book was he quoting?

    a) Numbers
    b) Deuteronomy
    c) Psalms
    b) Proverbs

6. Zechariah prophesied that in the last days, what will become of the tongues of Jerusalem's foes?

    a) they will resort to babble
    b) they uncontrollably will worship Christ
    c) they will burn with the wrath of the Lord
    d) they will rot in their mouths

7. Jewish law stipulated that something was true if how many witnesses stated it?

    a) two
    b) three
    c) four
    d) six

8. Paul compared the gifts of tongues and prophesy in a letter to
_____ .

   a) the Romans
   b) the Corinthians
   c) the Galatians
   d) Timothy

9. James wrote that the tongue is untamable, "an unruly evil, full
of _____ ."

   a) vulgar lies
   b) utter deceit
   c) deadly poison
   d) dark mischief

10. True or False: John in Revelation says the masses who gather to
praise the Lamb will speak in the same tongue.

Town and Country
I

1. Peniel was the place where:

   a) Cane slew Abel
   b) Jacob wrestled with God
   c) Joseph's brothers threw him into the pit
   d) Samson killed a lion

2. Where was Moses working as a shepherd when God spoke to
him from the burning bush?

   a) Tarshish
   b) Crete
   c) Midian
   d) Egypt

3. It was here that the Israelite elders approached Samuel and
demanded a king.

   a) Ramah
   b) Padanaram
   c) Bethshan
   d) Megiddo

4. The Philistine giant Goliath's hometown was _____ .
   a) Bethlehem
   b) Alexandria
   c) Elah
   d) Gath

5. When Samuel died, he was buried in his hometown, _____ .
   a) Sidon
   b) Ramah
   c) Jerusalem
   d) Jericho

6. In the 18th chapter of his book, Isaiah the prophet described Egypt as a land _____ .
   a) drowning in sand
   b) likened unto Hades
   c) shadowing with wings
   d) beneath the earth

7. The miraculous preservation of Daniel in the lion's den occurred where?
   a) Jericho
   b) Joppa
   c) Kedesh
   d) Babylon

8. Where was David born?
   a) Jericho
   b) Bethlehem
   c) Nazareth
   d) Jerusalem

9. An angry mob once tried to throw Jesus off a cliff. This occurred near _____ .
   a) Bethlehem
   b) Nazareth
   c) Tyre
   d) Jerusalem

10. Where were the two disciples going when Jesus appeared to them on the road after His resurrection?

    a) to Jericho
    b) to Emmaus
    c) to Damascus
    d) to Nazareth

Town and Country
II

1. Cain built a city and named it _____ .

    a) Enoch
    b) Gad
    c) Beersheba
    d) Cana

2. The "Oak of Weeping," which overlooked the grave of Rebekah's nurse, was at _____ .

    a) Bethel
    b) Padanaram
    c) Gibeon
    d) Beersheba

3. What was the significance of the field of Machpelah?

    a) it's where Cain slew Abel
    b) it's where Isaac met Rebekah
    c) it's where Abraham, Isaac, Jacob, and their wives were buried
    d) it's where Jacob built an altar after wrestling with God

4. Where did Hannah commit her son Samuel to the Lord?

    a) Jericho
    b) the River Jordan
    c) Mount Carmel
    d) Shiloh

5. In what town in Galilee did Jesus live during his ministry?

    a) Gergesa
    b) Magdala
    c) Bethsaida
    d) Capernaum

6. Jesus encountered blind Bartimaeus on the road outside
_____ .

   a) Nazareth
   b) Jericho
   c) Cana
   d) Gadara

7. What was the hometown of Lazarus, Mary, and Martha?

   a) Nazareth
   b) Jerusalem
   c) Bethany
   d) Capernaum

8. Where did the Pentecost occur?

   a) Cana
   b) Jerusalem
   c) Nain
   d) Philadelphia

9. What was the significance of Philadelphia in the New Testament?

   a) the birthplace of Paul
   b) a city where Paul made his headquarters for seven years
   c) a city Paul condemned
   d) one of the seven churches with which God communicated in Revelation

10. Revelation was inspired on which Mediterranean island?

   a) Crete
   b) Cyprus
   c) Patmos
   d) Sicily

Town and Country
III

1. What was Abraham's hometown?

   a) Babylon
   b) Ur
   c) Tyre
   d) Gomorrah

2. What was an early name for Jerusalem?

    a) Kadesh Barnea
    b) Sela
    c) Heshbon
    d) Salem

3. Name one of the two cities the Egyptians forced the enslaved Israelites to build.

4. After destroying Jericho, Joshua's army next took what city?

    a) Gibeon
    b) Hebron
    c) Ai
    d) Jerusalem

5. Where did Boaz live?

    a) Jericho
    b) Hebron
    c) Bethlehem
    d) Heshbon

6. King Hiram, who exchanged gifts with Solomon, ruled what city-state?

    a) Babylon
    b) Tyre
    c) Damascus
    d) Ramothgilead

7. "For I, saith the Lord, will be unto her a wall of fire round about . . ." Through the prophet Zechariah, God made that vow concerning what place?

    a) the kingdom of Israel
    b) Jerusalem
    c) the temple in Jerusalem
    d) the inner sanctuary of the temple in Jerusalem

8. What was the hometown of Philip, Andrew, and Peter?

    a) Tiberias
    b) Joppa
    c) Bethany
    d) Bethsaida

9. When Barnabas and Paul preached at Salamis, on what island were they?

    a) Crete
    b) Cyprus
    c) Patmos
    d) Sicily

10. Paul's followers Aristarchus and Secundus were Christians from
    _____ .

    a) Asia
    b) Thessalonica
    c) Corinth and Philippi, respectively
    d) Rome

Trees and Flowers
I

1. True or False: God created man and woman before He created plant life.

2. What two trees did God place in the center of the Garden of Eden?

    a) the trees of peace and war
    b) the trees of good and evil
    c) the trees of health and happiness
    d) the trees of life and knowledge

3. What kind of wood did God tell Noah to use in building the ark?

4. What kind of wood did God tell Moses to use in building the Ark of the Covenant?

5. The infant Moses survived Pharaoh's infanticide order thanks to an ark his mother fashioned of _____ .

    a) ash
    b) oak saplings
    c) bulrushes
    d) willow boughs

6. After miraculously escaping from Egypt through the parted Red Sea, the Israelites wandered three days in the wilderness before finding fresh water. When they finally came to Marah, the water there was too bitter to drink until God commanded Moses to sweeten it by throwing in a _____ .

   a) ginger root
   b) pine root
   c) tree
   d) lily

7. Under what kind of tree did Deborah sit when she held court?

   a) walnut
   b) palm
   c) willow
   d) sycamore

8. What Old Testament country was noted for its splendid cedar trees?

   a) Egypt
   b) Lebanon
   c) Syria
   d) Persia

9. The saddened Israelites in captivity hung up their harps on the branches of _____ trees.

   a) fig
   b) willow
   c) cherry
   d) cedar

10. "[T]hey toil not, neither do they spin: And yet I say unto you, That even Solomon in all his glory was not arrayed like one of these." What kind of flowers was Jesus describing in this passage?

   a) begonias
   b) roses
   c) pansies
   d) lilies

Trees and Flowers
II

1. What, exactly, was the forbidden fruit Adam and Eve ate?

    a) pear
    b) apple
    c) plum
    d) not known

2. "And he shall be like a tree planted by the rivers of water, that bringeth forth his fruit in his season . . ." To whom was the psalmist referring?

    a) God
    b) God's chosen king
    c) the coming Christ
    d) the person who delights in God's law

3. The prophet Jeremiah described a tree planted by waters that remains fruitful and green even in drought. Whom did this tree represent?

    a) the coming Christ
    b) the person who prays constantly
    c) the person who trusts in the Lord
    d) the person who delights in God's law

4. What kind of tree did Zacchaeus climb in order to see Jesus over the heads of the crowd?

5. The prophet Zechariah chastised, "[H]owl, O ye oaks of _____ ; for the forest of the vintage is come down."

    a) Gilead
    b) Bashan
    c) Jerusalem
    d) Sidon

6. Jesus startled Nathanael by seeing him at a great distance beneath a _____ tree.

    a) walnut
    b) cypress
    c) fig
    d) willow

7. Jesus scoffed at these spices, offered as tithes by the scribes and Pharisees.

    a) curry, rosemary, sage
    b) mint, anise, cumin
    c) coriander, basil, chives
    d) fennel, cinnamon, oregano

8. Jesus' disciples shocked the Pharisees by eating an impromptu Sabbath Day meal in a _____ .

    a) cornfield
    b) vineyard
    c) fig orchard
    d) cabbage patch

9. In his letter to the Romans, Paul compares God's people to what kind of tree?

    a) fig
    b) willow
    c) olive
    d) Tree of Life

10. Revelation discloses that the leaves on the Tree of Life are for _____ .

    a) shading the weary
    b) showing God's abundance
    c) showing God's omniscience
    d) healing

Vital Statistics

1. The great flood was caused by how many days and nights of rain?

    a) twelve
    b) twenty-five
    c) forty
    d) ninety

2. How many decks high was Noah's ark?

3. When King Solomon dedicated the temple, how many oxen and sheep did he order to be sacrificed?

    a) 142
    b) 1,420
    c) 14,200
    d) 142,000

4. What do Bible statisticians find interesting about Lamentations?

    a) the number of verses in each chapter is divisible by eleven
    b) every verse contains seventeen Hebrew words
    c) the second (and only the second) verse of each chapter refers to weeping
    d) the seventh and twelfth verses of each chapter are identical

5. What is the longest book in the Bible (in English)?

6. What is the shortest book in the Bible (in English)?

7. What is the longest verse in the Bible (in English)?

8. What is the shortest verse in the Bible (in English)?

9. In the parable of the talents, how many talents did each of the three servants initially receive, respectively?

    a) five, two, one
    b) ten, five, one
    c) ten, five, two
    d) ten, eight, five

10. The Bible tells us Solomon produced how many proverbs and songs?

    a) 46 proverbs, 21 songs
    b) 107 proverbs, 810 songs
    c) 21 proverbs, 46 songs
    d) 3,000 proverbs, 1,005 songs

Waterways

1. At creation, how much of the earth was covered with water?

    a) approximately seventy percent
    b) approximately thirty percent
    c) all of it
    d) none of it

2. Hounded by His thirsty people camped at Rephadim and Kadesh, God commanded Moses to make a stream of water gush from _____ .

    a) deserts
    b) mountains
    c) oak trees
    d) rocks

3. King David, fleeing his son Absalom, passed over this brook outside Jerusalem.

    a) Shiloh
    b) Saluda
    c) Kidron
    d) Bethsaida

4. Near what body of water did Elijah ascend to heaven?

    a) the River Nile
    b) the River Jordan
    c) the Dead Sea
    d) the Sea of Galilee

5. What king was noted for his construction of city waterworks?

    a) Solomon
    b) Sennacherib
    c) Esarhaddon
    d) Hezekiah

6. In Song of Solomon, the writer curiously described his beloved's eyes as "like the fishpools in _____ ."

    a) Ramothgilead
    b) Megiddo
    c) Heshbon
    d) Rabbah

7. Isaiah prophesied that what nation would overflow Judah like a flood?

    a) Israel
    b) Assyria
    c) Phoenicia
    d) Egypt

8. Where did John the Baptist do his baptizing?

    a) River Jordan
    b) River Tigris
    c) Sea of Galilee
    d) Dead Sea

9. When Jesus told the story of the rich man and Abraham, who was he talking to?

    a) the Romans
    b) the Pharisees
    c) the Jews
    d) the Gentiles

10. According to Revelation, the sixth angel will dry up this river by pouring his vial upon it.

    a) Jordan
    b) Tigris
    c) Euphrates
    d) Ganges

Wayward Paths

1. Where did Noah's descendants decide to build the Tower of Babel?

    a) Nod
    b) Egypt
    c) Punon
    d) Shinar

2. The rejected Esau became the father of what tribe?

    a) Philistines
    b) Edomites
    c) Sodomites
    d) Israelites

3. How did Moses punish the Israelites for making the golden calf while he was on Mount Sinai?

    a) ordered the sacrifice of 3,000 of the finest lambs

    b) ordered the execution of 100 family leaders

    c) ground the idol into powder, put it in water and made them drink it

    d) he didn't; he simply foretold that the Lord would make them wander four more years

4. The sins of Eli's sons were particularly abominable because they:

    a) were committed directly against God

    b) were committed against one another

    c) were committed directly against Eli

    d) were committed as Eli lay dying

5. God slew Judah's oldest son because he "was evil in the sight of the Lord." What was his name?

6. Proverbs teaches that a man succumbing to the temptation of a prostitute is like _____ .

    a) a house with no foundation

    b) an ox bound for slaughter

    c) a stream that changes course

    d) Adam and Eve duped by the serpent

7. Christ foretold that people blithely will ignore the signs of His second coming, just as people in the Old Testament times of _____ and _____ ignored impending doom.

    a) Noah and Lot

    b) Jacob and Joseph

    c) Jericho and Ai

    d) Israel and Judah

8. This one-time follower of Paul deserted the apostle and returned to worldly ways.

    a) Timothy

    b) Tychicus

    c) Carpas

    d) Demas

9. Which apostle predicted that in the end times, scoffers will mock the idea of a second coming?

    a) John

    b) Paul

    c) Peter

    d) James

10. In Revelation, the people of the world follow a seven-headed beast because:

    a) it provides them with food during the worst famine in history
    b) it recovers from a seemingly fatal wound
    c) the antichrist commands them to
    d) it offers them a life-preserving mark

A Way with Words

1. Jacob spoke briefly but eloquently of his sixth son, remarking that "he giveth goodly words." Which son was this?

    a) Gad
    b) Levi
    c) Napthali
    d) Zebulon

2. This prophet likened the Word of God to "a hammer that breaketh the rock in pieces."

    a) Isaiah
    b) Jeremiah
    c) Obadiah
    d) Micah

3. Luke gives us the first reported words of Jesus Christ: "How is it that ye sought me?" What was the occasion?

4. When the scribes and Pharisees brought an adulterous woman before Jesus and asked His opinion regarding her punishment, He leaned over and wrote in the sand. What did He write?

    a) Let he who is without sin cast the first stone.
    b) Go, and sin no more.
    c) Let it be so.
    d) the Bible doesn't report what He wrote

5. "Jesus of Nazareth the King of the Jews" was written on Christ's cross in what languages?

    a) Greek and Latin
    b) Aramaic and Latin
    c) Hebrew and Latin
    d) Hebrew, Greek, and Latin

6. To what did Jesus liken the temple defiled by moneychangers?

    a) a bed of serpents
    b) a lair of wolves
    c) a den of thieves
    d) an unclean sacrifice

7. Jesus likened Himself to a vine, his followers to _____

    a) grapes
    b) branches
    c) wine
    d) leaves

8. Paul suffered from "a thorn in the flesh." What did that mean?

    a) he had a burden to bear for Christ
    b) he had cancer
    c) he had arthritis
    b) not clarified in Scripture

9. Paul told the Hebrews that the word of God is _____ .

    a) soothing as cool water
    b) like a healing balm
    c) as a thorn in the flesh
    d) sharper than any two-edged sword

10. In writing to the Thessalonians, Paul warned against forged correspondence containing _____ .

    a) Christ's teachings taken out of context
    b) lies about Paul
    c) prophesy about Christ's return
    d) fabricated laws

What's in a Name?
I

1. God changed Abram's name to Abraham, meaning _____ .

    a) Father of a Great Multitude
    b) One Who Has Found Salvation
    c) Brightest Star
    d) Leader

2. Rachel named her first son Joseph, signifying her hope that
   _____ .

   a) the child would grow to subdue his older half-brothers
   b) the child would win his father's heart
   c) her sister Leah would bear no more children to Jacob
   d) God would add to her another son

3. God changed Jacob's name to Israel after Jacob:

   a) cursed Him
   b) fought Him
   c) forsook Him
   d) prayed to Him for a new name

4. Moses named his first son Gershom, meaning _____ .

   a) stranger
   b) gift
   c) ruddy
   d) pale

5. God replied "I Am That I Am" to which person who insisted on
   knowing His name?

   a) Abraham
   b) Jacob
   c) Moses
   d) Jonah

6. "The Preacher" spoke in the book of _____ .

   a) Leviticus
   b) Deuteronomy
   c) Ecclesiastes
   d) Lamentations

7. What famous Old Testament author is believed to have been "The
   Preacher"?

8. Writing this name restored Zacharias' ability to speak.

   a) John
   b) Yahweh
   c) Jesus
   d) Abraham

9. Jesus changed Simon Peter's name to Cephas, meaning
_____ .

    a) floating vessel
    b) sinking vessel
    c) rock
    d) eagle

10. What infamous hill in the Holy Land has a name meaning "Place of the Skull"?

What's in a Name?
II

1. Eve's name signified _____ .
    a) man's companion
    b) man's rib
    c) mother of all living
    d) daughter of God

2. True or False: The Bible refers to God as, among other things, an anchor.

3. True or False: The Bible refers to God as, among other things, a spear.

4. True or False: The Bible refers to God as, among other things, a horn.

5. When this son was born to her servant Bilhah and her husband Jacob, Rachel gave him a name meaning "my wrestling," commemorating her contentions with her sister Leah. Which son was he?
    a) Benjamin
    b) Gad
    c) Joseph
    d) Napthali

6. Who named Moses?
    a) his mother
    b) Miriam
    c) Pharaoh
    d) Pharaoh's daughter

7. Jesus' disciples called Him rabbi, meaning _____ .

    a) God
    b) Emanuel
    c) servant
    d) teacher

8. Why was the bedeviled man named Legion?

    a) because he commanded a Roman legion
    b) because he was the purser for a Roman legion
    c) because many spirits possessed him
    d) because he recorded the Judean census

9. Barnabas had another name:

    a) Peter
    b) Joses
    c) Bartholomew
    d) Silas

10. After Paul healed a man at Lystra, the astonished people there called him _____ and his companion Barnabas _____ .

    a) Abraham/Moses
    b) Isaiah/Jeremiah
    c) Isaiah/Daniel
    d) Mercury/Jupiter

What's in a Name?
III

1. True or False: God named each of the animals after placing Adam in the Garden of Eden.

2. Who was the first unborn child recorded in the Bible for whom an angel of God commanded a specific name?

    a) Ishmael
    b) Samuel
    c) John the Baptist
    d) Jesus

3. Just before she died giving birth, Rachel named the infant _____ , signifying her sorrow, but his father Jacob changed the name to Benjamin.

    a) Reuel
    b) Benoni
    c) Omar
    d) Kenaz

4. Joseph's older brothers had an unflattering nickname for him:

    a) yearling
    b) pet
    c) dreamer
    d) idler

5. If his parents' relatives and neighbors had gotten their way, what would have been John the Baptist's name?

    a) Simeon
    b) Zacharias
    c) Simon
    d) Jesus

6. At Bethlehem, Naomi gave herself a new name, Mara, based on her:

    a) conviction that Jesus would be born there
    b) bitter lot in life
    c) family surname
    d) instructions from God's angels

7. God through Nathan commanded young Solomon to be called _____ , or "Beloved of the Lord."

    a) Amnon
    b) Jonadab
    c) Jedidiah
    d) Ahimaaz

8. Which prophet referred to God as "the Ancient of days"?

    a) Isaiah
    b) Jeremiah
    c) Ezekiel
    d) Daniel

9. Who referred to the antichrist as "that man of sin . . . the son of perdition"?

    a) Daniel
    b) Jesus
    c) Paul
    d) John

10. In Revelation, John refers to Jesus as "the _____ of the tribe of Judah."

    a) Lion
    b) Lamb
    c) Root
    d) Flower

Who Said That?

I

1. "The Lord God of heaven hath given me all the kingdoms of the earth; and he hath charged me to build him an house at Jerusalem . . ." Who said that?

    a) King Saul
    b) King David
    c) King Cyrus
    d) Jesus

2. The Lord will roar from Zion "and utter his voice from Jerusalem." Which two prophets said that—one at the conclusion of his book, the other at the beginning?

    a) Joel and Amos
    b) Nahum and Habakkuk
    c) Isaiah and Jeremiah
    d) Isaiah and Haggai

3. "Fear not: for, behold, I bring you good tidings of great joy, which shall be to all people." Who said that?

    a) Jeremiah
    b) the apostle John
    c) an angel
    d) none of the above

4. Which prophet described God's punishment of Israel by famine as "cleanness of teeth in all your cities"?

   a) Isaiah
   b) Hosea
   c) Amos
   d) Nahum

5. "Prepare ye the way of the Lord, make his paths straight." Who said that?

   a) Moses
   b) Gideon
   c) Jeremiah
   d) John the Baptist

6. "[M]y conscience is captive to the Word of God. I neither can nor will recant . . ." Who said that?

   a) Barnabas
   b) Paul
   c) Stephen
   d) none of the above

7. Who said not "one jot or one tittle" of the Old Testament law would be forgotten "till all be fulfilled"?

   a) Jesus
   b) John the Baptist
   c) Peter
   d) Pontius Pilate

8. "Woman, why are you weeping? Whom are you looking for?" Who said that?

   a) the angel Gabriel
   b) Jesus
   c) a Roman guard
   d) Nathan

9. Who said "faith without works is dead"?

   a) Isaiah
   b) Jesus
   c) Paul
   d) James

10. "We love him, because he first loved us." Who said that?

    a) Peter
    b) Paul
    c) James
    d) John

Who Said That?
II

1. "For you are dust, and to dust you shall return." Who said that?

    a) God
    b) Samuel
    c) Job
    d) Bildad

2. "Am I my brother's keeper?" Who said that?

    a) Cain
    b) Reuben
    c) Adonijah
    d) Absalom

3. "[W]hither thou goest, I will go; and where thou lodgest, I will lodge . . ." Who said that?

    a) Sarai
    b) Rebekah
    c) Rachel
    d) Ruth

4. "How beautiful on the mountains are the feet of the one who brings . . . good news, who announces salvation . . ." Who said that?

    a) David
    b) Solomon
    c) Isaiah
    d) John the Baptist

5. "I am crucified with Christ." Who said that?

    a) Peter
    b) Paul
    c) the second thief at Calvary
    d) none of the above

6. Who made reference to a dead man being lifted up to the "bosom of Abraham"?

   a) Samuel
   b) David
   c) Jesus
   d) the apostle John

7. "You cannot serve God and mammon." Who said that?

   a) Isaiah
   b) Jeremiah
   c) Daniel
   d) Jesus

8. "Get thee behind Me, Satan!" Jesus said that . . . to whom?

   a) Peter
   b) Thomas
   c) Judas
   d) none of the above

9. "But they that wait upon the Lord shall renew their strength; they shall mount up with wings as eagles . . ." Who said that?

   a) Job
   b) Isaiah
   c) John the Baptist
   d) Jesus

10. "For we brought nothing into this world, and it is certain we can carry nothing out." Who said that?

    a) Job
    b) Nahum
    c) Ezekiel
    d) Paul

Who Said That?
III

1. "Ye shall not surely die." Who said that?

   a) Jesus
   b) Peter
   c) Paul
   d) Satan

2. "For the great day of his wrath is come; and who shall be able to stand?" Who said that?

   a) Moses
   b) Isaiah
   c) John
   d) Jesus

3. "Behold the Lamb of God, which taketh away the sin of the world." Who said that?

   a) God
   b) Jesus
   c) John the Baptist
   d) Peter

4. "Except a man be born again, he cannot see the kingdom of God." Jesus said that to whom?

   a) Zacchaeus
   b) Nicodemus
   c) Peter, Andrew, and James
   d) His assembled apostles

5. "For God so loved the world, that he gave his only begotten Son . . ." Whose repeated questioning led Jesus to say this?

   a) Zacchaeus
   b) Nicodemus
   c) Peter, Andrew, and James
   d) His assembled apostles

6. "The harvest truly is plenteous, but the labourers are few." Who said that?

   a) Abraham
   b) Joseph, son of Jacob
   c) John the Baptist
   d) Jesus

7. "Greet ye one another with an holy kiss." Who said that?

   a) Job
   b) Mary the mother of Jesus
   c) Mary Magdalene
   d) Paul

8. "All these things will I give thee, if thou wilt fall down and worship me." Who said that to whom?

   a) God to Abraham
   b) Pharaoh to Joseph
   c) Joseph to his brothers
   d) Satan to Christ

9. "Silver and gold have I none; but such as I have I give thee." Who said that?

   a) Jesus
   b) Peter
   c) John the Baptist
   d) the apostle John

10. "I have sinned in that I have betrayed the innocent blood." Who said that?

   a) Doeg
   b) Haman
   c) Judas
   d) Paul

Who Said That?
IV

1. "Let the day perish wherein I was born . . ." Who said that?

   a) Cain
   b) Job
   c) Jonah
   d) Judas

2. "How long wilt thou sleep, O sluggard? When wilt thou arise out of thy sleep?" Who said that?

   a) God
   b) Pharaoh
   c) Jesus
   d) the author of Proverbs

3. "And I will bless them that bless thee, and curse him that curseth thee . . ." God said this to whom?

   a) Adam
   b) Abram
   c) Jacob
   d) Moses

4. "[W]ist ye not that I must be about my Father's business?" Jesus said that to whom?

5. "Can there any good thing come out of Nazareth?" Who scoffingly asked that?

   a) King Herod
   b) Pontius Pilate
   c) Peter
   d) Nathanael

6. "For the Son of man is come to seek and to save that which was lost." Jesus said that to whom?

   a) Zacchaeus
   b) Nicodemus
   c) Peter, Andrew, and James
   d) His assembled apostles

7. "For the love of money is the root of all evil." Who said that?

   a) Solomon
   b) Haggai
   c) Jesus
   d) Paul

8. "I have fought the good fight, I have finished my course, I have kept the faith . . ." Who said that?

   a) David
   b) Job
   c) Jesus
   d) Paul

9. "[O]ne day is with the Lord as a thousand years, and a thousand years as one day." Who said that?

   a) Jesus
   b) Matthew
   c) Luke
   d) Peter

10. "For whosoever is born of God overcometh the world." Who said that?

    a) Jeremiah
    b) Jesus
    c) John
    d) Paul

Who Said That?
V

1. "Nation shall rise against nation . . . " Who said that?

    a) Moses
    b) Abraham
    c) Paul
    d) Jesus

2. "[A]s for me and my house, we will serve the Lord." Who said that?

    a) Noah
    b) Abram
    c) Joshua
    d) Job

3. "Hearken unto the voice of the people in all that they say unto thee: for they have not rejected thee, but they have rejected me, that I should not reign over them." Who said that to whom?

    a) God to Moses
    b) God to Samuel
    c) David to Solomon
    d) Jesus to His disciples

4. "Naked came I out of my mother's womb, and naked shall I return thither: the Lord gave, and the Lord hath taken away; blessed be the name of the Lord." Who said that?

    a) Noah
    b) Abram
    c) Job
    d) David

5. "We have found the Messiah." Who said that?

    a) the shepherds at Christ's birth
    b) the wise men at Christ's birth
    c) Judas
    d) Andrew

6. "Lord, I believe; help thou mine unbelief." Who said that?

    a) Peter
    b) Thomas
    c) the father of a child Jesus exorcised
    d) Martha

7. "Who then can be saved?" Who asked that?

    a) Job
    b) Jesus
    c) Jesus' disciples
    d) Paul

8. "[B]lessed are they that have not seen, and yet have believed." Jesus said that to whom?

    a) the congregation at the Sermon on the Mount
    b) the priests in the temple at Jerusalem
    c) Peter
    d) Thomas

9. ". . . God is no respecter of persons: But in every nation he that feareth him, and worketh righteousness, is accepted with him." Who said that?

    a) Jesus
    b) John
    c) Peter
    d) Paul

10. "Sirs, what must I do to be saved?" Who asked Paul and Silas that?

    a) Nicodemus
    b) Cornelius
    c) their jailer
    d) a Roman soldier who sheltered them at Athens

Who Said That?
VI

1. "[M]uch study is a weariness of the flesh." Who said that?

   a) the author of Deuteronomy
   b) the author of Proverbs
   c) the author of Ecclesiastes
   d) not found in Scripture

2. "The wolf also shall dwell with the lamb, and the leopard shall lie down with the kid; and the calf and the young lion and the fatling together; and a little child shall lead them." Who said that?

   a) Elijah
   b) Isaiah
   c) Jesus
   d) the apostle John

3. "[L]et not the sun go down upon your wrath." Who said that?

   a) God through Moses and Aaron
   b) the writer of Proverbs
   c) Jesus
   d) Paul

4. "For, lo, thou shalt conceive, and bear a son; and no razor shall come on his head . . ." An angel of God said that to whom?

   a) the mother of Isaac
   b) the mother of Samson
   c) the mother of Samuel
   d) the mother of John the Baptist

5. "What is truth?" Who asked that?

   a) Jesus
   b) Nicodemus
   c) Pontius Pilate
   d) Paul

6. "I know thy works, that thou art neither cold nor hot: I would thou wert cold or hot." This was said to whom?

   a) the Saducees
   b) the Pharisees
   c) the Jews at Jerusalem
   d) the church at Laodicea

7. "When thou was young, thou girdest thyself, and walkedst whither thou wouldest: but when thou shalt be old, thou shalt stretch forth thy hands, and another shall gird thee, and carry thee whither thou wouldest not." Jesus said that to whom?

    a) the multitude at the Sermon on the Mount
    b) the Jewish leaders in the temple
    c) Pontius Pilate
    d) Peter

8. "[W]hy persecutest thou me?" Who asked that?

    a) Daniel
    b) Jonah
    c) Saul/Paul
    d) God

9. "I can do all things through Christ which strengtheneth me." Paul said that to whom?

    a) the Romans
    b) the Philippians
    c) the Colossians
    d) the Thessalonians

10. "Thou believest that there is one God; thou doest well: the devils also believe, and tremble." Who said that?

    a) James
    b) Peter
    c) John
    d) Jesus

Who Said That?
VII

1. "In the beginning . . . ," the first words of Genesis, also are the first words of which New Testament book?

    a) Matthew
    b) John
    c) Romans
    d) Revelation

2. ". . . God loveth a cheerful giver." Who said that?

   a) Solomon
   b) Zephaniah
   c) Jesus
   d) Paul

3. "[A]nd your sons and your daughters shall prophesy, your old men shall dream dreams, your young men shall see visions." Who said that?

   a) God
   b) Jesus
   c) Elijah
   d) Joel

4. "For I know that my redeemer liveth, and that he shall stand at the latter day upon the earth." Who said that?

   a) Job
   b) Daniel
   c) Peter
   d) Paul

5. "Be ye not unequally yoked together with unbelievers: for what fellowship hath righteousness with unrighteousness?" Who said that?

   a) God through Moses and Aaron
   b) Elisha
   c) Jesus
   d) Paul

6. "Blessed art thou among women, and blessed is the fruit of thy womb." Who said that to Mary, Jesus' mother?

   a) God
   b) God's angel
   c) Elisabeth
   d) Simeon

7. "[I]t is better to marry than to burn." Who said that?

   a) David
   b) Solomon
   c) Jesus
   d) Paul

8. "There hath no temptation taken you but such as is common to man . . ." Who said that?

   a) Elisha
   b) Jesus
   c) Paul
   d) James

9. "Draw nigh to God, and he will draw nigh to you." Who said that?

   a) Eli
   b) David
   c) James
   d) Peter

10. "And because I tell you the truth, ye believe me not." Who said that?

   a) Cain
   b) Joseph, son of Jacob
   c) King Saul
   d) Jesus

Who Said That?
VIII

1. "Surely the Lord is in this place, and I knew it not." Who said that?

   a) Jacob
   b) King Saul
   c) King Nebuchadnezzar
   d) Thomas

2. "I am slow of speech, and of a slow tongue." Who made this excuse to God, hoping to dodge a commission?

   a) Noah
   b) Abram
   c) Moses
   d) Jonah

3. "Why hast thou troubled us? the Lord shall trouble thee this day." Who said that?

    a) Abraham
    b) Jacob
    c) Moses
    d) Joshua

4. "[Flor the joy of the Lord is your strength." Who said that?

    a) Nehemiah
    b) Jeremiah
    c) Hezekiah
    d) Obadiah

5. "There is a way which seemeth right unto a man, but the end thereof are the ways of death." Who said that?

    a) Ezra
    b) Solomon
    c) the apostle John
    d) Peter

6. "Except the Lord build the house, they labour in vain that build it . . ." Who said that?

    a) a psalmist
    b) Isaiah
    c) Jeremiah
    d) Jesus

7. "Paul, thou art beside thyself; much learning doth make thee mad." Who told Paul that?

    a) God
    b) Peter
    c) Festus
    d) no one

8. "When I was a child, I spake as a child, I understood as a child, I thought as a child: but when I became a man, I put away childish things." Who said that?

    a) David
    b) Simeon
    c) Jesus
    d) Paul

9. "He that is not with me is against me . . ." Who said that?

    a) Saul
    b) David
    c) Jesus
    d) Peter

10. "My kingdom is not of this world." To whom did Jesus say that?

    a) His disciples
    b) Pontius Pilate
    c) Satan
    d) the apostle John

Who Was I?

I

1. My name was Delilah. I was this judge's girlfriend.

    a) Jair's
    b) Jephtha's
    c) Abdon's
    d) Samson's

2. My name was Orpah. I lived before the time of King David and was _____ .

    a) Samson's sister
    b) Naomi's daughter-in-law
    c) King Saul's grandmother
    d) King Saul's mother

3. My name was Baruch. I was this person's secretary.

    a) Elisha's
    b) Jeremiah's
    c) Daniel's
    d) Paul's

4. Our names were Ethan. We both lived during time of King David and were _____ .

    a) heroic warriors
    b) temple musicians
    c) temple priests
    d) palace servants

5. My name was Ahinoam. I lived during the time of King David and was _____.

   a) King David's wife
   b) a court musician
   c) a temple priestess
   d) a palace servant

6. My name was Rizpah. I was a concubine of _____ .

   a) Esau
   b) Pharaoh
   c) Saul
   d) Solomon

7. My name was Amasa. After temporarily joining Absalom's failed revolt, I renewed my allegiance to my kinsman King David—but then was assassinated by _____ .

   a) Absalom's servant
   b) Adonijah
   c) Abigail
   d) Joab

8. My name was Vasti. I was a queen deposed by King _____ .

   a) David
   b) Solomon
   c) Ahasuerus
   d) Amon

9. My name was Malchus. I was _____ .

   a) the high priest's servant whose ear was cut off as Jesus was being arrested
   b) the high priest who arrested Jesus
   c) the man who accused Peter of being Jesus' disciple
   d) a Roman soldier who spat in Jesus' face

10. My name was Simon of Cyrene. I performed this unique deed.

   a) washed Jesus' feet
   b) gave my colt for Jesus to ride
   c) helped carry Jesus' cross
   d) offered my tomb for Jesus' burial

Who Was I?

II

1. My name was Potiphar. I was _____ .

   a) Joseph's master in Egypt
   b) a minor prophet
   c) the prophet Daniel's servant
   d) a Roman official who persecuted first-century Jews

2. My name was Jochebed. I was the mother of these two famous Old Testament brothers.

   a) Noah and Theo
   b) Jacob and Esau
   c) Moses and Aaron
   d) Absalom and Solomon

3. My name was Ashtoreth. In the time of the judges, I was a _____ .

   a) false goddess the Israelites worshipped
   b) fortune teller
   c) slave of Jephthah
   d) wife of Jephthah

4. My name was Gomer. In Old Testament times, I was _____ .

   a) a warrior
   b) a simple man who nonetheless reflected God's truth
   c) the wife of Hosea
   d) Nahum's quiet sister

5. My name was Salome. I was one of the women who:

   a) wove the curtains for the rebuilt temple in Jerusalem
   b) served the Last Supper
   c) partook of the Last Supper
   d) took spices to Jesus' tomb

6. My name was Jerahmeel. I was one of the soldiers sent by King Jehoiakim to arrest _____

   a) Baruch and Jeremiah
   b) Isaiah
   c) Ezekiel
   d) Shadrach, Meshach, and Abednego

7. My name was Rhoda. In the days of the early church, I was
   _____ .

   a) a leader of a house church in Antioch
   b) a servant in the home of Mary, the mother of John Mark
   c) a daughter of a prison guard who helped Peter escape
   d) a daughter of a prison guard who helped Paul and
   Barnabas escape

8. My name was Apollos. I was a _____ .

   a) Greek god
   b) Roman god
   c) first-century Christian teacher and preacher
   d) Roman centurion converted to Christianity

9. My name was Sosthenes. A hapless beating victim of Jewish
   leaders who unsuccessfully sought to prosecute Paul, I was a
   _____ .

   a) servant of the Roman governor Gallio
   b) synagogue leader
   c) companion of Paul
   d) merchant who happened to be traveling through Achaia
   at the wrong time

10. My name was Aristarchas. I was _____ .

   a) one of the priests who condemned Jesus
   b) a first-century Roman governor
   c) a Corinthian opponent of Paul
   d) a companion of Paul

Who Was I?
III

1. My name was Zerah. My birth as a twin was marked by this
   extraordinary feature.

   a) I emerged from the womb clutching my brother's heel
   b) I emerged from the womb with a red string tied to my
   hand
   c) I emerged from the womb speaking in sentences
   d) I emerged from the womb stillborn, but I mysteriously
   revived

2. My name was Eleazar. I succeeded my father, _____ , as a high priest.

   a) Samuel
   b) Aaron
   c) Melchizedek
   d) Ananias

3. My name was Dagon. I was the chief pagan god worshipped by the _____ .

   a) Israelites while Moses was on Mount Sinai
   b) Israelites after the death of Joshua
   c) Egyptians
   d) Philistines

4. My name was Barzillai. I was one of King David's _____ .

   a) best soldiers
   b) worst enemies
   c) benefactors
   d) brothers

5. My name was Jedidiah. I was a great king whose other (and best-known) name was _____ .

   a) David
   b) Solomon
   c) Cyrus
   d) Nebuchadnezzar

6. Our names were Bezalel and Oholiab. During the Exodus, we were _____ .

   a) thieves who attacked the encamped Israelites
   b) two of God's chosen craftsmen
   c) brothers of Joshua
   d) brothers of Moses and Aaron

7. My name was Cleopas. I was one of Jesus' _____ .

   a) brothers
   b) accusers
   c) disciples
   d) executioners

8. My name was Julius. I was a kind guard who escorted
   _____ .

   a) Joseph
   b) Jeremiah
   c) Paul
   d) Peter

9. My name was Barsabas. I was a candidate to become
   _____ .

   a) Roman governor of Palestine
   b) Roman governor of Greece
   c) leader of the church in Ephesus
   d) Judas' successor with the apostles

10. My name was Drusilla. I was the wife of the Roman governor
    _____ .

    a) Tiberias
    b) Felix
    c) Pontius Pilate
    d) Lysanias

Who Was I?
IV

1. A famous ruler called me Zaphnathpaaneah, but you know me
   better by my birth name:
   a) Joseph
   b) Elijah
   c) Samuel
   d) Daniel

2. My name was Cozbi. Aaron's grandson killed me with a spear
   and thereby:
   a) started a war
   b) stopped a war
   c) started a plague
   d) stopped a plague

3. My name was Peninnah. Like Hanna, I:

    a) was barren

    b) had a son named Samuel

    c) was married to Elkanah, Samuel's father

    d) was the mother of a famous leader in the days of the judges

4. My name was Ishbosheth. For two years, I was king of Israel and a rival of _____

    a) King David

    b) King Jeroboam

    c) King Rehoboam

    d) King Asa

5. My name was Sherah. I built three cities and was the daughter of _____ .

    a) Asher

    b) Ephraim

    c) Jonah

    d) Nero

6. My name was Candace. I was queen of _____ .

    a) Ethiopia

    b) Crete

    c) Thebes

    d) Macedonia

7. My name was Huldah. I was a _____ in Judah.

    a) sorcerer

    b) prophetess

    c) queen of a city-state

    d) golden idol

8. My name was Tertius. I was Paul's _____ .

    a) jailer

    b) executioner

    c) scribe

    d) ship captain

9. My name was Jason. I got into trouble by:

    a) criticizing Noah

    b) criticizing Balaam

    c) sheltering Paul and Silas

    d) stealing sacrificial items

10. My name was Pethuel. I was the father of the prophet
_____ .

    a) Daniel
    b) Hosea
    c) Joel
    d) Habakkuk

Who Was I?
V

1. My name was Ahiam. I lived during the time of King David and
was _____ .

    a) a heroic warrior
    b) a temple musician
    c) a temple priest
    d) a palace servant

2. I was the first Deborah named in Scripture. Buried beneath
Allonbachuth, or the "Oak of Weeping," I was _____ .

    a) Sarah's servant
    b) Isaac and Rebekah's daughter
    c) Isaac and Rebekah's daughter-in-law
    d) Rebekah's nurse

3. Our names were Jannes and Jambres. Paul, in a letter to Timothy,
identified us as "men of corrupt minds, reprobate concerning the
faith." We had lived many years earlier and had been opponents
of _____ .

    a) Abraham
    b) Moses
    c) David
    d) Solomon

4. My name was Magog. A malevolent subject of end times prophesy, I was a grandson of _____ .

    a) Noah
    b) Isaac
    c) Jacob
    d) Moses

5. My name was Amraphel. I was an ancient king who:

    a) oversaw construction of the Tower of Babel
    b) died in the great flood
    c) let Jacob dwell in my land during his exile
    d) went to war against Sodom and Gomorrah

6. My name was Julia. I was among the Christians whom Paul greeted in _____ .

    a) Colosse
    b) Ephesus
    c) Philippi
    d) Rome

7. My name was Shalmaneser. As king of this country, I besieged and conquered Samaria.

    a) Egypt
    b) Macedonia
    c) Judah
    d) Assyria

8. My name was Nebuzaradan. Captain of the guard under King Nebuchadnezzar, I was commanded to:

    a) take the king's life to avoid capture and torture
    b) burn Jerusalem
    c) assassinate Jeremiah
    d) assassinate Gedaliah

9. My name was Gamaliel. I taught the law to _____ .

    a) Dan
    b) Ezra
    c) Daniel
    d) Saul/Paul

10. My name was Demetrius. At Ephesus, I was a _____ .

    a) Roman guard
    b) Roman governor
    c) silversmith who made idols
    d) tent maker

Bonus Bible Hodgepodge

1. True or False: The term for heaven is not found in Genesis.

2. Cain was a _____ .
   a) shepherd
   b) crop farmer
   c) hunter
   d) vintner

3. Who holds the distinction as second-oldest human in the Bible?
   a) Methuselah
   b) Enoch
   c) Jared
   d) Lamech

4. How many of each animal did God command Noah to take aboard the ark?
   a) one pair
   b) seven pairs
   c) one pair of clean animals, seven pairs of unclean animals and birds
   d) one pair of unclean animals, seven pairs of clean animals and birds

5. What prompted Abram and Lot to separate?
   a) a feud over young women to marry their sons
   b) insufficient grazing land for their livestock
   c) invasion by an enemy army
   d) a commandment from God

6. While living in the wilderness of Paran, Ishmael became a noted
   _____ .
   a) farmer
   b) prophet
   c) archer
   d) stone mason

7. Where was Abraham buried?
   a) in a cave
   b) beneath a small pyramid
   c) he wasn't; he was cremated
   d) he wasn't; he was lifted physically beyond the clouds

8. What was Jacob's dying request?

    a) that Joseph forgive his brothers
    b) that Joseph's brothers forgive Joseph
    c) that Pharaoh grant Jacob's descendants a large, fertile tract of land (believed by historians to have been in the Sinai Peninsula)
    d) that his sons bury him in Canaan

9. When He gave them the promised land, God instructed the Israelites to vanquish the Canaanites; otherwise, the Canaanites figuratively would become:

    a) like a plague of locusts
    b) like cancer
    c) like thorns in the Israelites' sides
    d) like poison

10. What excuse did Jonah offer for dodging the Lord's command that he go to Nineveh?

    a) he was too young
    b) he was too old
    c) poor eyesight
    d) no excuse

11. In detailing the Passover ritual, did God prescribe leavened or unleavened bread?

12. True or False: Old Testament law said interest rates could not be charged when lending to the poor.

13. For what purpose did Moses establish the tabernacle of the congregation (the meeting tent)?

    a) as the place for him and Aaron to meet with the tribal elders
    b) as the place for feasts and weddings to be held
    c) as the place for adjudicating disputes
    d) as the place for the Israelites to confer with God

14. True or False: Old Testament law prohibited tatooing.

15. Whatever happened to Aaron's rod?

    a) it was buried with him
    b) it was buried with his brother Moses
    c) it was placed in the Ark of the Covenant
    d) the Lord took it from Aaron because of Israel's backsliding

16. This ancient king, a "remnant of the giants," required an extra-large bed.

    a) Saul
    b) Ahasuerus
    c) Asa
    d) Og

17. True or False: Samson was a gambling man who made a riddle to his guests and bet forty acres of land that they couldn't solve it at his bridegroom's feast.

18. What was Saul doing when the Lord identified him to Samuel as the man who would become Israel's first king?

    a) fighting the Philistines
    b) looking for his father's donkeys
    c) reveling at a party
    d) watering his family's livestock

19. David's best friend was _____ .

    a) Samson
    b) Jonathan
    c) Gideon
    d) Nimrod

20. What person in the Bible is reported to have weighed his hair?

    a) Samson
    b) Absalom
    c) Herod I
    d) Nero

21. When the captive Israelites returned to Jerusalem to rebuild the city, who paid for the rebuilding of the temple?

    a) Ezra
    b) the high priests
    c) heads of families and King Cyrus
    d) King Darius

22. Job had three opinionated but not-so-helpful friends. Their names: _____ , _____ , and _____ .

23. What book appears last in the Old Testament?

24. How old was Methuselah when he died?

    a) 461
    b) 761
    c) 969
    d) 1,058

25. Moses and Aaron were _____ .

    a) stonemasons
    b) brothers
    c) enemies
    d) unknown to each other because they lived at different
       times

26. Of all Jesus' miracles, which one (besides His resurrection) is
    included in all four Gospel accounts?

    a) raising Lazarus from the dead
    b) walking on water
    c) feeding 5,000 with loaves and fishes
    d) healing the woman who touched His garment

27. In the parable of the good Samaritan, where was the victim
    going when he was attacked by thieves?

    a) from Jerusalem to Jericho
    b) from Tarshish to Bethlehem
    c) from Tyre to Sidon
    d) from Sodom to Gomorrah

28. The word Abba, spoken by Jesus and others, means
    _____ .

    a) Christ
    b) Divine
    c) Protector
    d) Father

29. The scribes and Pharisees criticized Jesus because His disciples
    failed to adhere to this mealtime custom.

    a) washing their hands before eating
    b) giving thanks
    c) drinking wine with the meal
    d) sitting cross-legged

30. True or False: None of the books of the Bible were penned per-
    sonally by Jesus.

31. This Roman leader's image was on the coin Jesus used for one of his illustrations.

    a) Herod's
    b) Pontius Pilate's
    c) Caesar's
    d) Nero's

32. How long does the psalmist say is our average lifespan?

    a) 110 years
    b) 90 years
    c) 70 years
    d) 40 years

33. Proverbs 30 confides there are four things the writer fails to understand. Which of the following is not among them?

    a) the way of a lion on the prowl
    b) the way of a snake on a rock
    c) the way of a ship in mid-ocean
    d) the way of a man with a maiden

34. Jesus is known to have used what weapon in a moment of anger?

    a) sword
    b) stone
    c) whip
    d) fire

35. What prompted Jesus to use this weapon?

    a) false teachings of imposters who claimed to be Christ
    b) overly cruel punishment of a servant by a Roman soldier
    c) overly cruel treatment of a child by a Jewish merchant
    d) money changing in the Jerusalem temple

36. Jesus once dined with a Pharisee named _____ .

    a) Shaul
    b) Theophilus
    c) Jaddua
    d) Simon

37. Name the three components of the Holy Trinity.

38. How did the apostles choose Judas' successor?

    a) prayer
    b) drawing lots
    c) prayer and drawing lots
    d) message from an angel

39. It's vital for our salvation that our names be entered in God's book of:

    a) names
    b) truth
    c) days
    d) life

40. Don't look: What's the last word in the Bible (KJV, NKJV, NASB, NIV, NRSV, TLB, NCV)?

Answers

Angels

1. b) Hagar (Genesis 16:7-14)
2. False (2 Samuel 24:15-17)
3. d) morning star (Isaiah 14:12)
4. c) Gabriel (Daniel 8)
5. b) disturbed the water (John 5:2-4)
6. c) the reapers (Matthew 13:39)
7. a) children (Matthew 18:10)
8. True (Luke 22:42-43)
9. c) judge (1 Corinthians 6:3)
10. c) strangers (Hebrews 13:1-2)

Animals I

1. b) ram (Genesis 22:13)
2. d) cows (Genesis 41:1-4)
3. c) bees (Deuteronomy 1:44)
4. a) to destroy the Philistines' crops (Judges 15:4-5)
5. c) ravens (1 Kings 17:2-6)
6. b) female bears (2 Kings 2:23-24)
7. d) great fish (Jonah 1:17)
8. a) donkey (Numbers 22:22-31)
9. b) doves (Matthew 21:12-13)
10. b) locusts (Revelation 9:3-11)

Animals II

1. a) behemoth (Job 40:15-17)
2. b) Dan (Genesis 49:16-17)
3. b) quail (Exodus 16:11-13)
4. d) ostrich (Job 39:13-18)
5. c) horse (Job 39:19)
6. b) swine (Matthew 8:28-34)
7. c) a hen gathers her chicks (Matthew 23:37)
8. True (Mark 16:16-18)
9. b) scorpions (Luke 10:19)
10. c) goats (Matthew 25:32)

Authority

1. d) Melchizedek (Genesis 14:18)
2. c) told him how the Lord had already delivered David from a bear and lion (1 Samuel 17:32-37)
3. a) Eliakim (Isaiah 22:20-24)
4. b) the authority to make decisions on earth that would be binding in heaven (Matthew 16:19)
5. "Render therefore unto Caesar the things which be Caesar's, and unto God the things which be God's." (Luke 20:25)
6. c) because God, the ultimate power, has ordained these lesser powers (Romans 13:1-7)
7. d) Paul (2 Timothy 3:16)
8. c) Timothy (1 Timothy 2:1-2)
9. c) Titus (Titus 2:15)
10. d) Peter (1 Peter 2:13-14)

Blessings

1. b) laughed (Genesis 17:15-17)
2. a) Asher would produce food worthy of royalty (Genesis 49:20)
3. c) not to be thorough when reaping and gathering in their harvests (Leviticus 19:9-10)
4. a) Aaron (Numbers 6:22-26)
5. c) quail (Numbers 11:16-32)
6. b) obey His commandments (Deuteronomy 28:13)
7. d) both of the above (Esther 8:1-2)
8. b) Simeon (Luke 2:25-26)
9. c) poor in spirit (Matthew 5:2-3)
10. c) Nazareth (Matthew 13:53-58)

Books of the Old Testament I

1. Leviticus
2. Numbers (Numbers 1:1-46)
3. c) Leviticus and Deuteronomy (Leviticus 19:18, Deuteronomy 6:5)
4. a) Canaan
5. 23rd
6. 150
7. Psalm 119
8. Psalm 117
9. 2 Samuel 22
10. b) 57 and 60

Books of the Old Testament II

1. a) Leviticus (Leviticus 16:5-10)
2. b) Ruth
3. 31
4. Ecclesiastes 3
5. c) Daniel (Daniel 5)
6. Jeremiah
7. d) Jerusalem (Lamentations 1:8)
8. a) Obadiah
9. d) Nineveh (Nahum 1:1)
10. c) begins with a complaint and ends with a psalm

Books of the Old Testament III

1. b) Numbers (Numbers 16)
2. c) Deuteronomy (Deuteronomy 34)
3. b) Judges (Judges 3:9-11)
4. c) Ruth (Ruth 4:13-17)
5. d) 1 Samuel and 1 Chronicles (1 Samuel 8-31, 1 Chronicles 8-10)
6. d) Esther
7. d) Job (Job 41)
8. a) Isaiah (Isaiah 40:22)
9. Daniel, Hosea, Joel, Amos, Obadiah, Jonah, Micah
10. c) Joel (Joel 1)

Books of the New Testament

1. c) with Paul in Rome under house arrest, preaching and teaching (Acts 28:16-31)
2. Galatians, Ephesians, Philippians, Colossians
3. 1 and 2 Thessalonians
4. c) he wrote part of it in large letters (Galatians 6:11)
5. b) Galatians (Galatians 5:22-23)
6. a) the church at Colosse (Colossians 1:2)
7. c) Thessalonians (2 Thessalonians 3:10)
8. b) 1 Thessalonians (1 Thessalonians 4:16)
9. d) by Paul to Timothy (1 Timothy 1:1-2, 2 Timothy 1:1-2)
10. False—Philemon was a slave owner. (Philemon)

Christ's Birth and Early Life

1. c) Judaea (Luke 2:4)
2. Herod (Matthew 2:1)
3. a) Egypt (Matthew 2:13-14)
4. d) Simeon (Luke 2:25-26)
5. Anna (Luke 2:36-38)
6. "God with us." (Matthew 1:23)
7. c) Jerusalem (Luke 2:41-50)
8. c) increasing in wisdom and stature (Luke 2:52)
9. d) the Holy Spirit (Matthew 4:1)
10. a) angels (Matthew 4:11)

Christ's Followers I

1. c) treasurer for the group (John 13:28-29)
2. a) walked on water (Matthew 14:25-31)
3. Thomas (John 20:24-29)
4. a) pledged his love for Christ (John 21:15-17) (For those of
    you who thought the answer was "d", the cock appears
    to have crowed only once or twice, or an unspecified
    number of times, depending on the book of the Gospels.)
5. b) Peter and John (John 20:1-4)
6. John (John 20:4)
7. c) Matthias (Acts 1:21-26)
8. c) Italy (Acts 27:1)
9. False (Matthew 10:2-4)
10. d) John (Revelation 1:1-2)

Christ's Followers II

1. c) Nathanael (John 1:47)
2. a) Peter (Matthew 8:14-15)
3. b) fishing (Matthew 4:18-22)
4. c) sons of thunder (Mark 3:17)
5. Peter (Matthew 16:18-19)
6. d) James (Matthew 17:1-2)
7. c) they feared the Jews (John 20:19)
8. c) attacks by lions (2 Corinthians 11:23-29)
9. True (Acts 28:1-6)
10. b) Peter's decision to stop associating with non-Jews
    (Galatians 3:11-21)

Christ's Last Days, Crucifixion and Resurrection I

1. d) to prepare Him for burial (Matthew 26:6-13)
2. b) He sweated blood (Luke 22:44)
3. c) Jewish leaders (Matthew 26:14-16, 47-48)
4. b) washed his hands (Matthew 27:24-26)
5. d) JESUS OF NAZARETH THE KING OF THE JEWS (John 19:19)
6. a) theft (Matthew 27:38)
7. True (John 19:34)
8. d) a caretaker (John 20:11-16)
9. b) Jewish leaders bribed them (Matthew 28:11-15)
10. d) honey and fish (Luke 24:42-43)

Christ's Last Days, Crucifixion, and Resurrection II

1. c) Judas (John 12:4-5)
2. clothes (Matthew 21:8)
3. b) spikenard (Mark 14:3)
4. d) fell over backward (John 18:1-6)
5. b) flung it into the temple in a rage (Matthew 27:5)
6. c) would fight for Him (John 18:36)
7. b) they gambled for His clothes (Matthew 27:35)
8. d) broke their legs (John 19:32-33)
9. c) Nicodemus (John 19:38-42)
10. "Peace be unto you." (John 20:19)

Christ's Miracles

1. b) wedding (John 2:1-11)
2. His mother (John 2:3-5)
3. c) throw Him off a cliff (Luke 4:16-30)
4. b) calming a storm at sea (Mark 4:39)
5. a) Jairus (Mark 5:22-43)
6. c) healing the sick woman who touched the hem of His garment (Mark 5:22-43)
7. Matthew 14:22-33, Mark 6:45-51, John 6:16-21
8. c) four days (John 11:39)
9. a) in a fish's mouth (Matthew 17:24-27)
10. c) He told them where to fish (John 21:1-11)

Christ's Travels and Ministry

1. the Gospels: Matthew, Mark, Luke, John
2. False—to save it (John 12:47)
3. c) Nicodemus (John 3:3-4)
4. b) heal the sick (Luke 9:1-6)
5. b) deny/cross (Matthew 16:24)
6. d) Zacchaeus didn't invite Jesus to dinner; Jesus invited Himself to Zacchaeus' house (Luke 19:1-10)
7. b) because Jesus and His clothes became radiant (Matthew 17:1-9, Mark 9:2-9, Luke 9:28-36)
8. Moses and Elijah (Matthew 17:1-3, Mark 9:2-4, Luke 9:28-31)
9. c) over the death of Lazarus (John 11)
10. c) tombs (Matthew 23:27)

Cloak and Dagger I

1. False—Laban tricked Jacob, but Jacob fled from Laban (Genesis 31)
2. a) Rahab (Joshua 2:1)
3. b) Ehud (Judges 3:12-30)
4. Delilah (Judges 16:4-21)
5. b) Endor (1 Samuel 28:7-25)
6. b) David and Saul's respective army commanders (2 Samuel 8:16, 1 Samuel 14:50, 2 Samuel 3:27)
7. d) all of the above (2 Samuel 18:9-15)
8. True (1 Kings 11:40)
9. c) Queen Jezebel (1 Kings 19:1-2)
10. a) Amaziah (2 Kings 14:1-6)

Cloak and Dagger II

1. Cain slaying his brother Abel (Genesis 4:8)
2. Esau (Genesis 27)
3. d) idols (Genesis 31:19-20)
4. c) beneath her, packed aboard a camel (Genesis 31:34-35)
5. b) twenty pieces of silver (Genesis 37:28)
6. d) by making it appear Benjamin had stolen Joseph's own silver cup (Genesis 44:1-2)
7. c) Jael (Judges 4:17-22)
8. Shibboleth (Judges 12:5-6)
9. c) for supporting David against Saul (1 Samuel 22:6-19)
10. a) Athaliah (2 Kings 11:1-16)

Cloak and Dagger III

1. Lot's two daughters (Genesis 19:15-16)
2. d) let them die in a plague (Numbers 14:36-38)
3. c) the sword with which David had killed Goliath (1 Samuel 21:8-9)
4. c) Bathsheba (1 Kings 1:11)
5. a) Hazael (2 Kings 8:14-15)
6. a) Joram and Ahaziah (2 Kings 9:23-27)
7. d) Sennacherib (2 Kings 19:37)
8. b) Jehoshabeath (2 Chronicles 22:10-12)
9. c) Gedaliah (2 Kings 25:22-26)
10. d) he was lowered over the side of the city wall in a basket under the cover of darkness (Acts 9:25)

Clothing

1. b) Jacob's (Genesis 27:15-16)
2. c) the edges shouldn't be trimmed (Leviticus 19:27)
3. d) the same clothes for forty years (Deuteronomy 29:5)
4. b) a new coat (1 Samuel 2:19)
5. c) David's servants (1 Chronicles 19:4)
6. d) Zephaniah (Zephaniah 1:8)
7. c) it was seamless (John 19:23-24)
8. a) silk (Proverbs 31:22)
9. d) pearls (1 Timothy 2:9)
10. True (1 Corinthians 11:15)

Colors

1. c) red (Genesis 25:25)
2. blue, purple, scarlet (Exodus 26:1)
3. d) red (Numbers 19:1-2)
4. b) blue (Ezekiel 23:6)
5. c) scarlet/purple (Matthew 27:28, Mark 15:17)
6. a) white (Matthew 28:3)
7. b) emerald (Revelation 4:3)
8. a) white (Revelation 4:4)
9. b) white (Revelation 6:1-2)
10. Death (Revelation 6:8)

Conversions

1. d) his nails grew long as bird claws (Daniel 4:33)
2. False (John 3:3)
3. d) 3,000 (Acts 2:41)
4. c) Ananias (Acts 9:10-19)
5. d) Sergius Paulus (Acts 13:6-12)
6. c) Macedonia (specifically, Philippi; Acts 16:9-15)
7. c) an earthquake that decimated his prison and thus could have brought about his downfall (Acts 16:25-40)
8. a) Athens (Acts 17:22-34)
9. b) burned their magic books (Acts 19:19)
10. c) Thessalonians (1 Thessalonians 1:9)

Creation

1. b) earth and sky (Genesis 1:1)
2. c) "Let there be light." (Genesis 1:3)
3. a) third (Genesis 1:9-13)
4. d) none of the above (they are for signs) (Genesis 1:14)
5. c) sixth (Genesis 1:26-30)
6. c) the land creatures (Genesis 1:24-31)
7. False—He made man in the image of Himself (Genesis 1:26)
8. that it was very good (Genesis 1:31)
9. c) to have children (Genesis 1:27-28)
10. b) with a pervasive mist (Genesis 2:6)

Crime and Punishment I

1. b) "stripe for stripe" (Exodus 21:25)
2. b) repaying with five oxen (Exodus 22:1)
3. a) pay double the worth of the property to the other (Exodus 22:9)
4. c) death (Exodus 21:15)
5. c) death (Exodus 21:17)
6. True (Exodus 21:14)
7. True (Exodus 21:13)
8. c) death (Exodus 21:16)
9. a) compensation for any losses and support of the victim during convalescence (Exodus 21:18-19)
10. b) if the ox had a prior record of meanness, both you and your ox must be put to death, unless the victim's family agreed to accept restitution; if it was the ox's first offense, your ox must be slaughtered but you would not face personal punishment (Exodus 21:28-30)

Crime and Punishment II

1. c) he slew the Egyptian (Exodus 2:11-12)
2. c) Sabbath breaking (Numbers 15:32-36)
3. d) death (Exodus 22:18)
4. a) utter destruction (Exodus 22:20)
5. b) Numbers (Numbers 35:6)
6. c) execution (Joshua 10:26)
7. d) Bethshemesh (1 Samuel 6:19)
8. c) Shimei (1 Kings 2:36-46)
9. True (Proverbs 6:30)
10. b) Jesus (Matthew 18:15)

Curses and Condemnations

1. d) the serpent (Genesis 3:14)
2. c) loss of his preeminence as oldest son (Genesis 49:3-4)
3. b) their anger and cruelty (Genesis 49:5-7)
4. True (Deuteronomy 27:17)
5. a) Joshua (Joshua 6:26)
6. b) leprosy (2 Kings 5)
7. d) would have no peace (Isaiah 48:22)
8. a) Hananiah (Jeremiah 28:15-17)
9. d) Capernaum (Matthew 11:23-24)
10. c) fig (Matthew 21:18-19)

Death

1. eating from the tree of knowledge of good and evil (Genesis 2:16-17)
2. c) Abel's (Genesis 4:8)
3. b) giving birth (Genesis 35:16-18)
4. b) Nabal (1 Samuel 25)
5. d) Queen Jezebel (2 Kings 9:32-34)
6. c) one of the psalmists (Psalm 89:48)
7. Herod's (Matthew 2:13-15)
8. a) Jesus' (Matthew 27:50-53)
9. False (Luke 24:46-48, Revelation 1:18)
10. d) the Ephesian and Colossian believers (Ephesians 2:1, Colossians 2:13)

Dreams and Visions

1. d) a dead man (Genesis 20:3)
2. a) Bethel (Genesis 28:10-19)
3. Joseph's (Genesis 37:5-24)
4. c) the lean cows ate the fat cows (Genesis 41:1-4)
5. d) divers vanities (Ecclesiastes 5:7)
6. b) Ezekiel (Ezekiel 1)
7. b) King Nebuchadnezzar's (Daniel 2, 4)
8. a) numbered, weighed, divided (Daniel 5:25-28)
9. d) Pilate's wife (Matthew 27:19)
10. a) animals (Acts 10:9-16)

The Early Church

1. d) Christ's second coming (Acts 3:20-21)
2. b) Claudius (Acts 18:2)
3. b) Ephesus (Acts 19:24-29)
4. d) he learned Paul was a Roman citizen (Acts 22:29)
5. c) baptize (1 Corinthians 1:17)
6. b) they should not cover their heads (1 Corinthians 11:4)
7. c) Philippi (Philippians 4:2)
8. b) Epaphroditus (Philippians 2:25)
9. d) Achaicus (1 Corinthians 16:17)
10. a) Lord, faith, baptism (Ephesians 4:5)

Ears to Hear

1. b) Jacob (Genesis 35:4)
2. d) a slave who intentionally forfeited freedom (Exodus 21:5-6)
3. b) to melt them and forge a golden calf (Exodus 32:2-4)
4. a) cursing (Leviticus 19:14)
5. idols and their makers (Psalm 115:4-8)
6. b) Ezekiel (Ezekiel 33:32)
7. b) by putting His fingers in the man's ears and speaking a command (Mark 7:33-35)
8. Garden of Gethsemane (Matthew 26:36-51, Mark 14:32-47, John 18:10)
9. c) faith (Romans 10:17)
10. d) speak/wrath (James 1:19)

Eyes to See

1. c) their nakedness (Genesis 3:7)
2. d) Isaac and Jacob (Genesis 27:1, 48:10)
3. True (Leviticus 21:16-18)
4. True (Leviticus 22:22)
5. False (Judges 16:23-30)
6. a) God through Moses (Deuteronomy 27:18)
7. d) righteous (Psalm 34:15)
8. d) Nebuchadnezzar (Jeremiah 39:5-7)
9. b) Bartimaeus (Mark 10:46-52)
10. c) something like scales that covered his eyes (Acts 9:18)

Faith and Trust

1. a) Asa (2 Chronicles 14:9-15)
2. "It is better to trust in the Lord than to put confidence in man."
3. b) possess the land (Isaiah 57:13)
4. c) mustard seed (Matthew 17:20)
5. d) "My Lord and my God." (John 20:28)
6. damned (Mark 16:16)
7. c) Abraham (Romans 4:9)
8. a) shield (Ephesians 6:16)
9. c) good fight (1 Timothy 6:12)
10. False. Jesus does, however, state that it is hard for those who trust in riches to enter into the kingdom of God. (Mark 10:24)

Famous Phrases

1. c) watchmen (Isaiah 52:8)
2. b) before the great flood (Genesis 6:4)
3. d) Job (Job 19:20)
4. c) Abraham (Genesis 15:15)
5. d) the Gospels, concerning the accusation that Jesus was devil-ridden (Mark 3:22-25)
6. a) the Pharisees and scribes (Luke 15:1-7)
7. c) they all "gave up the ghost" (Acts 5:5, 10; 12:20-23)
8. d) Paul (1 Corinthians 5:3)
9. a) Ezekiel (Ezekiel 18:2)
10. b) Jacob and his sons (Genesis 45:18)

Fire and Water

1. b) five months (Genesis 7:24)
2. c) that newborn Israelite males be drowned in the Nile (Exodus 1:22)
3. b) Zimri (1 Kings 16:18)
4. d) Zero (Daniel wasn't cast into a fiery furnace; Daniel 3)
5. d) a contentious man (Proverbs 26:21)
6. a) Jehoiakim (Jeremiah 36:21-23)
7. c) the guards were killed by the blaze, though the prisoners survived (Daniel 3:19-22)
8. c) Jacob's well (John 4:6)
9. c) 1 Kings 18
10. c) Pilate (Matthew 27:24)

Fish and Ships

1. d) no one (Genesis 7)
2. d) Zebulon (Genesis 49:13)
3. b) Tarshish (1 Kings 10:22)
4. d) harpoons and spears (Job 41:7)
5. c) Habakkuk (Habakkuk 1:15)
6. a) Egypt (Isaiah 19:1-8)
7. b) Tyrus (Ezekiel 26:4-5)
8. c) Sea of Tiberias (John 21:1)
9. c) 153 (John 21:11)
10. d) Adriatic Sea (Acts 27:27-41)

Food and Drink I

1. dust (Genesis 3:14)
2. b) bread (Exodus 16:4-31)
3. c) honey (Judges 14:5-9)
4. d) vinegar (Ruth 2:14)
5. d) Zarephath (1 Kings 17:8-16)
6. d) mocker (Proverbs 20:1)
7. locusts and honey (Matthew 3:4)
8. c) loaves and fishes (Matthew 14:15-21)
9. b) bread (Luke 22:19)
10. d) vinegar (John 19:28-30)

Food and Drink II

1. b) Noah (Genesis 9:4)
2. b) Noah (Genesis 9:20-27)
3. d) fins and scales (Deuteronomy 14:9-10)
4. a) raven (Deuteronomy 14:14)
5. False (Deuteronomy 14:19)
6. It was hallowed temple bread. (1 Samuel 21:1-6, Mark 2:25-26)
7. b) Solomon's (1 Kings 4:22-23)
8. c) salt (2 Kings 2:19-22)
9. d) honey (Ezekiel 2:8-3:3, Revelation 10:9-10)
10. False (there are no references to tomatoes in the Bible)

Food and Drink III

1. c) onions and garlic (Numbers 11:5)
2. d) loaves of bread/fig cakes (1 Samuel 25:18)
3. d) veal and unleavened bread (1 Samuel 28:21-25)
4. a) Solomon (1 Kings 10:21)
5. b) empty jars (2 Kings 4:1-7)
6. c) added meal (2 Kings 4:40-41)
7. a) wipe Jerusalem as a man wipeth a dish (2 Kings 21:13)
8. b) he had plenty of everything (Job 29:1-6)
9. c) apples (Song of Solomon 2:5)
10. b) Hosea (Hosea 7:8)

The Garden of Eden

1. Pison/Pishon, Gihon, Hiddekel/Tigris, Euphrates (Genesis 2:10-14)
2. b) to tend the garden (Genesis 2:15)
3. c) food (Genesis 2:16-17)
4. b) tree of knowledge of good and evil (Genesis 2:17)
5. to remove Adam's rib and create Eve from it (Genesis 2:21-22)
6. "the cool of the day" (Genesis 3:8)
7. c) the ground (Genesis 3:17)
8. d) nothing (Genesis 2:25)
9. c) with animal skin coats (Genesis 3:21)
10. b) to thwart human access to the tree of life (Genesis 3:24)

Gifts

1. Esau (Genesis 27)
2. b) Esau (Genesis 32:13-20, 33:8-11)
3. d) almonds (Genesis 43:11)
4. b) "ye walk in my statutes, and keep my commandments, and do them" (Leviticus 26:3)
5. c) Abigail (1 Samuel 25:18)
6. d) twenty cities in Galilee (1 Kings 9:11)
7. c) gold earrings and money (Job 42:11)
8. a) wisdom/knowledge (Daniel 2:21)
9. gold, frankincense, myrrh (Matthew 2:11)
10. d) rest (Matthew 11:28)

God's Commandments

1. d) to take off his shoes (Exodus 3:5)
2. c) Moses (Exodus 20)
3. Deuteronomy 5
4. d) the Israelites had been foreigners themselves in the land of Egypt (Exodus 22:21)
5. a) cast it to the dogs (Exodus 22:31)
6. b) The Great Commission (Matthew 28:19)
7. "Thou shalt love the Lord thy God with all thy heart, and with all thy soul, and with all thy mind." (Matthew 22:37)
8. d) Deuteronomy (Deuteronomy 6:5, 10:12, 30:6)
9. "Thou shalt love thy neighbor as thyself." (Matthew 22:39)
10. c) Leviticus (Leviticus 19:18)

God's Enemies

1. Nod (Genesis 4:16)
2. c) He destroyed their god Dagon and smote the Philistines with emerods, or tumors (1 Samuel 5)
3. d) dogs ate it (2 Kings 9:30-37)
4. Haman (Esther 7:10)
5. c) the families of Daniel's accusers (Daniel 6:24)
6. a) fox (Luke 13:32)
7. b) babbler (Acts 17:18)
8. d) Bernice (Acts 25:23)
9. c) he was struck down by an angel of the Lord and was devoured by worms (Acts 12:21-23)
10. d) they will be banished and punished forever (2 Thessalonians 1:7-9)

God's Love

1. d) 1,000 (Deuteronomy 7:9)
2. shepherd (Psalm 23:1)
3. d) life (Psalm 63:3)
4. b) Psalms (Psalm 107:8, 15, 21, 31)
5. a) Isaiah (Isaiah 66:13)
6. b) loving Jacob while hating Esau (Malachi 1:2-3)
7. His only begotten Son
8. c) the number of hairs on our heads (Luke 12:7)
9. d) cast all our cares on Him (1 Peter 5:7)
10. b) that we keep his commandments (1 John 5:3)

God's Modus Operandi I

1. with wind (Genesis 8:1)
2. d) wind (Exodus 14:21)
3. a) ashes (Exodus 9:8-9)
4. d) back (Exodus 33:20-23)
5. none
6. b) whirlwind (2 Kings 2:11)
7. d) Cyrus (Ezra 1:1-5)
8. c) in a beauty contest (Esther 1:10-2:18)
9. b) hatred for our children (Proverbs 13:24)
10. d) He temporarily struck Zacharias dumb
    (Luke 1:5-22, 57-64)

God's Modus Operandi II

1. a) to tend it (Genesis 2:15)
2. c) made an unworthy offering to God (Genesis 4:3-7)
3. c) Abraham's faith (Genesis 15:6)
4. b) because they were building a monument toward heaven
    (Genesis 11:1-9)
5. d) so Joseph eventually could save God's people from
    starvation (Genesis 50:20)
6. d) take off his shoes (Exodus 3:5)
7. a) burning incense improperly (Leviticus 10:1-2)
8. c) because Saul did not totally destroy the Amalekites as
    God had commanded (1 Samuel 15:3-11)
9. b) touched the sacred Ark of the Covenant (2 Samuel 6:6-7)
10. True (Job 1:6-12)

God's Wrath

1. a) flaming sword (Genesis 3:24)
2. Lot's wife (Genesis 19:26)
3. Caleb (Numbers 32:11-12)
4. d) killed in battle by the Philistines (1 Samuel 4:10-11)
5. c) King Ahab (1 Kings 16:33-17:1)
6. b) Nebuchadnezzar (2 Kings 25)
7. death (Romans 6:23)
8. b) beg the rocks and mountains to fall on them and hide them (Revelation 6:15-17)
9. a) tormented with fire and brimstone (Revelation 14:9-10)
10. d) John (Revelation 6:17)

Go Where I Send Thee

1. c) 400 (Genesis 15:13, Exodus 12:40, Acts 7:6)
2. forty (Numbers 32:13)
3. b) Moab (Numbers 22-24)
4. b) Nineveh (Jonah 1:1-2)
5. a) Jonah's (Jonah 1:12)
6. three days and nights (Jonah 1:17)
7. c) prayed (Jonah 2)
8. d) because it was in Judea that a mob had tried to stone Jesus (John 11:8)
9. b) Gentiles (Acts 26:16-18)
10. d) he appealed to Caesar, as was his right as a Roman citizen (Acts 25:10-12)

Grief

1. Hagar (Genesis 21:16)
2. b) Jacob (Genesis 42)
3. c) his daughter (Judges 11:30-40)
4. d) Hannah's (1 Samuel 1:1-18)
5. a) Amnon and Absalom (2 Samuel 13, 2 Samuel 18)
6. d) their captivity in Babylon (Psalm 137)
7. Jairus' daughter (Matthew 9:18-26)
8. c) went off in a boat to be alone (Matthew 14:13)
9. b) hearing the cock crow after his third denial of Christ (Matthew 26:74-75)
10. d) the apostle John (Revelation 21:4)

Heavenly Phenomena

1. b) bricks (Genesis 11:3-4)
2. False (Genesis 9:28-29)
3. Pleiades and Orion (Job 38:31)
4. b) Isaiah (Isaiah 13:13)
5. a) Amos (Amos 5:26)
6. d) Samaria (Luke 9:52-56)
7. c) lightning (Matthew 24:27)
8. c) Jesus (Luke 21:25)
9. c) three hours of daytime darkness (Luke 23:44-45)
10. d) Joel (Acts 2:19, Joel 2:30)

The Holy Spirit

1. b) Pharaoh (Genesis 41:38)
2. b) Samson (e.g., Judges 14:19, 15:14-15)
3. c) fire (Matthew 3:11)
4. a) Jesus (John 14:26)
5. d) that of a rushing mighty wind (Acts 2:1-4)
6. d) Simon of Samaria (Acts 8:5-24)
7. b) Asia and Bithynia (Acts 16:6-7)
8. love, joy, peace, patience, kindness, goodness, faithfulness, gentleness, self-control (Galatians 5:22)
9. b) the seal of His promise (Ephesians 1:13)
10. d) John/Revelation (Revelation 1:10-11)

Husbands and Wives

1. d) Leah (Genesis 29)
2. d) 14 years (Genesis 29:15-30)
3. True (Genesis 41:45)
4. c) Moses' (Exodus 2:21)
5. Nabal (1 Samuel 25)
6. b) Michal (2 Samuel 6:16)
7. d) Merab (1 Samuel 18:17-19)
8. c) they were all princesses (1 Kings 11:3)
9. c) Ananias and Sapphira (Acts 5:1-10)
10. b) Christ loves the church (Ephesians 5:25)

Hymns I

1. d) 1 Timothy (1 Timothy 1:17)
2. a) Isaiah (Isaiah 53:3)
3. b) Galatians (Galatians 6:14)
4. c) Lamentations (Lamentations 3:22-23)
5. a) Job (Job 19:25)
6. d) Revelation (Revelation 4:8)
7. c) Habakkuk (Habakkuk 2:20)
8. a) Micah (Micah 5:2)
9. b) Exodus (Exodus 33:22)
10. d) Revelation (Revelation 5:12)

Hymns II

1. a) Mark (Mark 8:34)
2. b) Psalms (Psalm 139:23)
3. c) 1 John (1 John 3:1)
4. b) Ezekiel (Ezekiel 34:26)
5. b) Jeremiah (Jeremiah 8:22)
6. d) 1 John (1 John 1:7)
7. a) Isaiah (Isaiah 64:8)
8. d) the writer of the Bible's longest Psalm (Psalm 119:19)
9. b) Exodus (Exodus 25:17-22)
10. c) Luke (Luke 24:29)

Kinfolk of the Old Testament I

1. a) Seth (Genesis 4:25)
2. b) grandfather (Genesis 5:25-29)
3. Esau and Jacob (Genesis 25:24-26)
4. c) daughter-in-law (Genesis 38:6)
5. Reuben (Genesis 37:21-22)
6. Mahlon and Kilion (Ruth 1:1-2)
7. c) daughter-in-law (Ruth 1:1-4)
8. 7 (1 Samuel 16:10-11)
9. a) nephew (1 Chronicles 2:15-16)
10. b) 42 (Matthew 1:17)

Kinfolk of the Old Testament II

1. c) Canaan (Genesis 9:22-25)
2. d) great-grandfather (Genesis 10:1-10)
3. False—the lineage of Shem (Genesis 11:10-27)
4. b) nephews of Abraham (Genesis 22:20-21)
5. a) Keturah (Genesis 25:1)
6. b) his sons Isaac and Ishmael (Genesis 25:9)
7. c) nephew and son-in-law (Genesis 29:10-20)
8. c) she had weak eyes (Genesis 29:17)
9. d) no immediate relation (Numbers 11:28)
10. True—they were brothers-in-law (1 Samuel 14:49, 18:27)

Kinfolk of the New Testament

1. Jesus (Luke 1:35-2:7)
2. James, Joses, Simon, and Judas/Judah (Matthew 13:55, Mark 6:3)
3. Lazarus (John 11:1-2)
4. c) Benjamin (Philippians 3:5)
5. d) no known relation (Acts 5, Acts 16)
6. b) Mary (Acts 12:12)
7. b) Barnabas (Acts 15:36-40, Colossians 4:10)
8. a) Jewish and Greek (Acts 16:1)
9. d) nephew (Acts 23:12-35)
10. b) Stephanas' (1 Corinthians 16:15)

Laws and Rituals

1. b) His angel passing over the blood-marked homes of the captive Israelites when killing the Egyptians' firstborn (Exodus 12:27)
2. True (Exodus 23:19)
3. True (Exodus 23:24)
4. c) eagle wings (Exodus 25:1-7)
5. a) death (Exodus 31:15, 35:2; Numbers 15:32-36)
6. b) anger at the Israelites and their golden calf (Exodus 32:19)
7. c) Jubilee (Leviticus 25:8-13)
8. a) with an ox and donkey yoked together (Deuteronomy 22:10)
9. a) clothes made of different materials in combination (Deuteronomy 22:11)
10. kindling a fire (Exodus 35:3)

Leaders I

1. c) Canaan (Genesis 50:4-6)
2. d) Mordecai and Esther (Esther 9:29-32)
3. the ant (Proverbs 6:6)
4. a) Benjamin (1 Samuel 9:1-2)
5. c) Solomon (1 Kings 10:1)
6. c) king of Babylon (2 Kings 24:11)
7. d) the writer of Proverbs (Proverbs 29:12)
8. a) Judah (1 Kings 15:23-24)
9. a) unknown causes (Deuteronomy 32:48-52, Deuteronomy 34:5-7)
10. c) cut the child in two with a sword (1 Kings 3:16-28)

Leaders II

1. c) Saul (1 Samuel 10:17-24)
2. b) David (2 Samuel 6:1-15)
3. b) Absalom (2 Samuel 15-18)
4. d) David promised him the throne (1 Kings 1:29-30)
5. True (1 Kings 3:4-14)
6. c) wealth and honor (1 Kings 3:10-13)
7. d) Israel (1 Kings 16:29-31)
8. False—it was the other way around (2 Kings 24:10-16, Ezra 1)
9. b) wicked return to idol worship (2 Chronicles 33)
10. a) King Artaxerxes (Nehemiah 2:1-8)

Light

1. False—it was first (Genesis 1-3)
2. b) God's Word (Psalm 119:105)
3. d) law (Proverbs 6:23)
4. b) the Gentiles (Isaiah 49:6)
5. c) John the Baptist (John 1:6-8)
6. b) the truthful (John 3:20-21)
7. c) God would be glorified (Matthew 5:16)
8. the eye (Luke 11:34)
9. c) Saul/Paul (Acts 9:1-8)
10. d) James (James 1:17)

Love

1. d) Jacob (Genesis 29-30)
2. d) a year (Deuteronomy 24:5)
3. b) "covereth all sins" (Proverbs 10:12)
4. c) Samaritans (John 4:9)
5. d) is forgiven (Luke 7:47)
6. b) Jewish leaders (John 5:18, 5:42)
7. faith and hope (1 Corinthians 13:13)
8. b) fear (1 John 4:18)
9. a) in deed and in truth (1 John 3:18)
10. c) Paul (1 Corinthians 16:20)

Mortals' Miracles

1. b) Aaron (Exodus 7:19-20)
2. d) lice (Exodus 8:16-17)
3. d) made it stand still for a whole day (Joshua 10:12-14)
4. Elijah (1 Kings 17:17-24) and Elisha (2 Kings 4:8-35)
5. c) Elijah's cloak (2 Kings 2:13-14)
6. a) faith (Matthew 21:21-22)
7. b) Peter healing a crippled man (Acts 3:1-8)
8. True (Acts 6:8)
9. c) Aeneas (Acts 9:32-34)
10. b) Dorcas (Acts 9:36-42)

Mountains

1. c) Ararat (Genesis 8:4)
2. b) Moriah (Genesis 22:2)
3. d) Horeb (Exodus 3:1)
4. Sinai (Exodus 19:20, 31:18)
5. b) Hor (Numbers 20:22-29)
6. d) Pisgah (Deuteronomy 34:1-4)
7. d) Elijah vs. the false prophets (1 Kings 18:20-40)
8. d) Hermon (Deuteronomy 4:48)
9. b) Olivet (2 Samuel 15:30)
10. d) not named (Matthew 28:16-20)

Music

1. True (Exodus 15:20)
2. d) none of the above (trumpets made of rams' horns; Joshua 6:4-5)
3. d) Saul (1 Samuel 10:5-6)
4. b) David's (1 Samuel 16:23)
5. c) Levites (2 Chronicles 5:12)
6. c) for his subjects to bow and worship his golden image (Daniel 3:7)
7. True (Matthew 26:30)
8. b) brass and cymbal (1 Corinthians 13:1)
9. True (Ephesians 5:19, Colossians 3:16)
10. d) trumpet (Revelation 8:2)

Obedience to God

1. eight (Genesis 7:13)
2. b) Noah (Genesis 8:20)
3. d) she turned to salt (Genesis 19:1-26)
4. b) Isaac (Genesis 22:1-19)
5. c) sacrifice their best products, carefully chosen and prepared (Leviticus 1:3, 2:1, 3:1, etc.)
6. sacrifices (1 Samuel 15:22)
7. b) Absalom (2 Samuel 15:1-6)
8. c) his wives (1 Kings 11:4)
9. d) refusing to dine on royal meat and wine (Daniel 1:8)
10. d) Stephen (Acts 7:54-60)

Occupations in the Old Testament

1. Abel (Genesis 4:2)
2. c) judge (Judges 3:31)
3. c) Nimrod (Genesis 10:9)
4. an Israelite judge (Judges 4:4)
5. a) shepherd (1 Samuel 16:11)
6. True (various psalms)
7. c) Jewish teacher and king's wine steward (Ezra 7:6, Nehemiah 1:11)
8. b) teacher/slave in King Nebuchadnezzar's court (Daniel 1:1-4)
9. a) shepherd (Amos 1:1)
10. b) livestock owner (Job 1:3)

Occupations in the New Testament

1. a) priest (Luke 1:8)
2. c) fisherman in the Sea of Galilee (Matthew 4:18)
3. d) doctor (Colossians 4:14)
4. b) religious leader (John 3:1)
5. b) beggar (Mark 10:46)
6. c) tax collector (Luke 19:1-2)
7. c) centurion (Acts 10:1)
8. d) cloth seller (Acts 16:14)
9. b) tent makers (Acts 18:1-3)
10. a) Ephesus (Acts 19:23-41)

Parents and Children I

1. b) Ishmael (Genesis 16:15)
2. c) Isaac (Genesis 25:1-2)
3. b) Rachel (Genesis 35:24)
4. b) Samuel (1 Samuel 1:20)
5. d) became ungodly men (1 Samuel 2:12-17)
6. c) Jesse (1 Samuel 16:1-13)
7. b) killed by Philistines (1 Samuel 31:2)
8. d) Bathsheba (2 Samuel 12:24)
9. a) Amoz (Isaiah 1:1)
10. Elisabeth (Luke 1:13)

Parents and Children II

1. a) Noah (Genesis 10:1)
2. d) David (2 Samuel 7:18-29)
3. a) Elkanah (1 Samuel 1:19-20)
4. b) Kish (1 Samuel 9:1-2)
5. c) Saul (1 Samuel 18:27)
6. b) Rehoboam (1 Kings 11:43)
7. c) she worshipped an idol (1 Kings 15:11-13)
8. d) Ahaz (2 Kings 16)
9. b) Beeri (Hosea 1:1)
10. John (John 19:26-27)

Parents and Children III

1. b) Lamech (Genesis 5:28-29)
2. c) Bathsheba (2 Samuel 12:15-18)
3. d) the Bible does not specify
4. d) Hiel (1 Kings 16:34)
5. c) killed them for food (2 Kings 6:24-30)
6. d) 10 (Job 1)
7. c) Jephtha's (Judges 11:29-40)
8. c) Uri (Exodus 31:2)
9. a) Loruhama (Hosea 1:6)
10. b) Eunice (2 Timothy 1:5)

Patriarchs

1. c) he didn't; God simply "took him" (Genesis 5:24)
2. Abraham (Genesis 12:2, Romans 4:1, etc.)
3. c) Jacob (Genesis 49:1-28)
4. a) Samuel (Genesis 49:1-28)
5. d) Canaan (Genesis 49:29-30)
6. Egypt (Genesis 50:26)
7. c) Moses (Exodus 4:24)
8. a) by deliberately collapsing a temple on top of himself and his enemies (Judges 16:23-30)
9. d) a double portion of Elijah's spirit (2 Kings 2:9-12)
10. d) David (2 Samuel 24:1-16)

Peoples of the Bible

1. b) descendants of Canaan (Genesis 9:25, Joshua 11:23)
2. a) Syrians (Genesis 25:20)
3. b) Hivites (Genesis 34)
4. b) Ishmaelites (Genesis 37:28)
5. c) they were giants (Numbers 13:33)
6. d) Moabites (Numbers 22:3-4)
7. d) Philistines (Judges 16:4-5)
8. c) Syrians (1 Kings 15:18)
9. b) Babylonians (2 Kings 20:12)
10. a) Sabeans (Job 1:15)

Persecution and Martyrdom

1. a) they were using the Israelites as slaves (Exodus 14:5)
2. d) Jezebel (1 Kings 18:4)
3. c) he worshipped God (Job 1:20)
4. d) James (Acts 12:1-2)
5. c) pray for them (Matthew 5:44)
6. a) Gamaliel (Acts 5:34-40)
7. b) by the sword (Acts 12:1-2)
8. a) they were pleased (Acts 12:1-3)
9. Saul/Paul (Acts 7:58)
10. c) Stephen (Acts 7:60)

Plagues and Afflictions

1. c) speech impediment (Exodus 4:10-16)
2. d) leprosy (Exodus 4:6-7)
3. b) leprosy (Numbers 12:1-10)
4. a) a bronze snake on a pole (Numbers 21:4-9)
5. d) he was lame (2 Samuel 9:3-6)
6. b) Asa (2 Chronicles 16:12-13)
7. c) falling through an upstairs lattice (2 Kings 1:2-4)
8. b) the pool of Bethesda (John 5:2-4)
9. a) Ananias (Acts 9:17-18)
10. d) James (James 5:14)

Prayer

1. c) Enos' (Genesis 4:26)
2. b) Abraham (Genesis 18:23-33)
3. d) because Moses was stalling when he should have been taking action (Exodus 14:15)
4. d) 51
5. c) Solomon (2 Chronicles 7:14)
6. d) dedication of the temple in Jerusalem (2 Chronicles 6-7)
7. c) vain repetitions (Matthew 6:7)
8. Matthew 6:9-13, Luke 11:1-4
9. a) three (2 Corinthians 12:8)
10. d) My grace is sufficient for thee (2 Corinthians 12:9)

Prophets and Prophesies I

1. d) swifter than leopards (Habakkuk 1:8)
2. d) Micah (Micah 5:2)
3. a) Isaiah (Isaiah 7:14)
4. b) Habakkuk (Habakkuk 2:1)
5. a) Isaiah (Isaiah 21:9)
6. a) Hosea (Hosea 1:2)
7. b) love his wife (Hosea 3:1)
8. c) Christ's entry into Jerusalem on a donkey
   (Zechariah 9:9)
9. fire (Matthew 3:11)
10. d) Revelation (Revelation 6:1-8)

Prophets and Prophesies II

1. d) 850 (1 Kings 18:19)
2. d) fire (2 Kings 2:11)
3. d) that mockers would gamble for His clothes beneath the
   cross (Psalm 22:18)
4. a) Jeremiah (Jeremiah 38:4-6)
5. d) His Word (Amos 8:11)
6. c) Haggai (Haggai 2:23)
7. d) Zechariah (Zechariah 12-14)
8. d) Zechariah (Zechariah 2:1-2)
9. b) Gabriel (Luke 1:19)
10. b) Gabriel (Luke 1:26)

Prophets and Prophesies III

1. d) farming (1 Kings 19:19-21)
2. c) fed a lot of people with a little bread (2 Kings 4:42-44)
3. a) Isaiah (Isaiah 24:20)
4. b) Isaiah (Isaiah 44:28)
5. a) Isaiah (Isaiah 53:3)
6. d) tremble (Jeremiah 10:10)
7. c) Obadiah (Obadiah 1:1)
8. b) Jonah (Jonah 3:4)
9. a) sat in ashes and repented (Jonah 3:5-10)
10. d) Zechariah (Zechariah 13:7, Matthew 26:31)

Revelation

1. a) the seven churches of Asia (Revelation 1:4)
2. c) 1,260 days (Revelation 11:3)
3. c) Michael (Revelation 12:7)
4. b) dragon (Revelation 12:9)
5. c) 666 (Revelation 13:18)
6. d) those who receive the mark of the beast (Revelation 14:11)
7. Armageddon (Revelation 16:16)
8. c) 1,000 years (Revelation 20:1-3)
9. b) sea (Revelation 21:1)
10. d) crystal (Revelation 22:1)

Riches

1. d) all of the above (Genesis 41:42)
2. c) silver, gold, and cloth (Exodus 12:35-36)
3. b) ivory (Amos 6:4)
4. c) 666 (1 Kings 10:14)
5. rubies (Proverbs 8:11)
6. "a good name" (Proverbs 22:1)
7. c) thieves (Matthew 6:19)
8. hearts (Matthew 6:21)
9. d) pearls (Matthew 7:6)
10. b) they were used to buy a graveyard for strangers (Matthew 27:3-7)

Servants

1. b) Abraham and Lot (Genesis 13:6-9)
2. c) Egypt (Deuteronomy 28:68)
3. b) Nabal (1 Samuel 25:9-11)
4. a) Ziba (2 Samuel 9:9-11, 2 Samuel 16:1-4, 2 Samuel 19:24-30)
5. d) Gehazi (2 Kings 5:20-27)
6. d) Cyrus (Ezra 1:1-4)
7. c) Hatach (Esther 4:5)
8. a) palsy (Matthew 8:5-13)
9. the washing of His disciples' feet (John 13:4-10)
10. b) Onesimus (Philemon 1:9-19)

Signs and Omens I

1. c) the dove did not return to the ark (Genesis 8:12)
2. d) creation of a rainbow in the clouds (Genesis 9:12-14)
3. She gave water to him and his camels. (Genesis 24:12-20)
4. Although it was aflame, it didn't burn up. (Exodus 3:2-3)
5. a) wool on a threshing floor (Judges 6:36-40)
6. b) Belshazzar (Daniel 5)
7. d) the manger scene (Luke 2:12)
8. d) Jesus (Matthew 16:2-3)
9. c) kiss (Matthew 26:47-49)
10. c) a comet temporarily blinded the Roman executioners (Matthew 27:50-53)

Signs and Omens II

1. d) a monument of twelve stones (Joshua 4:1-9)
2. c) gave away a shoe (Ruth 4:7)
3. b) by the way they drank water (Judges 7:1-8)
4. a) the shooting of arrows (2 Kings 13:15-19)
5. a) He set back the shadow of a sundial (2 Kings 20:8-11)
6. b) Isaiah (Isaiah 20:1-3)
7. d) shaking the dust from their feet (Matthew 10:14)
8. c) Jonah's three days inside the fish, symbolic of Jesus' pending three days of death (Matthew 12:38-41)
9. d) a piece of bread (John 13:26)
10. a) a seal on the forehead (Revelation 7:3)

Sins and Sinners

1. a) brimstone and fire rained from heaven (Genesis 19:24)
2. d) Gibeah (Judges 19)
3. b) calf (Exodus 32:1-4)
4. a) Amnon (2 Samuel 3:2, 2 Samuel 13:1-33)
5. b) Nathan (2 Samuel 12:1-10)
6. d) Naboth (1 Kings 21:1-16)
7. c) Isaiah (Isaiah 43:27)
8. a) his brother's wife (Matthew 14:3, Mark 6:17-18)
9. c) Herod's niece (Matthew 14:3-11)
10. c) adultery with the sinner's mother-in-law (1 Corinthians 5:1)

Sleep

1. stones (Genesis 28:11)
2. d) by requiring lenders to return to them each night cloaks that were offered as collateral for loans (Deuteronomy 24:10-13)
3. d) Moses' (Deuteronomy 31:16)
4. Samson (Judges 16:19)
5. c) His beloved people (Psalm 127:2)
6. b) their riches consume their thoughts (Ecclesiastes 5:12)
7. d) that no one be told, and that she be given something to eat (Mark 5:42-43)
8. c) praying (e.g., Matthew 26:36-46)
9. d) "The spirit indeed is willing, but the flesh is weak." (Matthew 26:41)
10. c) Jonah (Jonah 1:4-5)

Soldiers and Warfare I

1. b) Philistines (Deuteronomy 20:17)
2. d) none of the above; after being mortally wounded at Thebez, he ordered his armor bearer to stab him so it couldn't be said that he died by a woman's hand (Judges 9:52-54)
3. b) the armor was too cumbersome for him (1 Samuel 17:39)
4. True (1 Samuel 17:49)
5. b) sword (1 Samuel 17:51)
6. c) Abner (2 Samuel 2-3)
7. d) he killed himself (1 Samuel 31:4)
8. b) it was hung on a wall, then cremated (1 Samuel 31:8-13)
9. c) Abishai (2 Samuel 23:18)
10. a) donkeys' heads and doves' dung (2 Kings 6:24-25)

Soldiers and Warfare II

1. c) shout (Joshua 6:20)
2. a) Saul's son Jonathan (1 Samuel 14:24-30)
3. c) Goliath would fight the best Israelite soldier; the winner's army would subjugate the other, with no further fighting (1 Samuel 17:9)
4. a) Doeg (1 Samuel 22:18)
5. d) hanged himself (2 Samuel 17:23)
6. c) Benaiah (2 Samuel 23:20)
7. b) Lahmi (1 Chronicles 20:5)
8. c) with an angel (2 Kings 19:35)
9. b) 12,000 (2 Chronicles 9:25)
10. c) Israel (2 Chronicles 16:1)

Soldiers and Warfare III

1. c) twenty (Numbers 1:3)
2. b) was engaged to be married (Deuteronomy 20:7)
3. c) 300 (Judges 7:1-8)
4. d) because He knew that unless the victory was miraculous, the Israelites would credit themselves (Judges 7:2)
5. b) Rimmon (Judges 20:45, 21:13)
6. b) Valley of Salt (2 Samuel 8:13, 2 Kings 14:7)
7. a) his son Jonathan (1 Samuel 13:22)
8. b) throw his flesh to wild animals (1 Samuel 17:44)
9. a) spring (2 Samuel 11:1)
10. b) 3

Teachings I

1. c) godly fear (Psalm 111:10, Proverbs 1:7)
2. b) wisdom (Proverbs 4:7)
3. b) speech (Proverbs 15:1)
4. a) the virtuous woman (Proverbs 31)
5. d) all of the above (Job 21:13, Proverbs 21:17, Luke 8:14)
6. a) no prophet is welcome in his hometown (Luke 4:16-30)
7. c) a sequence of blessings (Matthew 5:3-12)
8. c) Jesus (Matthew 6:25-27)
9. a) judge you (Matthew 7:1-2)
10. b) free (John 8:32)

Teachings II

1. c) servants in the house of the Lord (Psalm 134)
2. c) heart (Proverbs 28:26)
3. d) those who are merciful (Matthew 5:7)
4. b) wolves in sheeps' clothing (Matthew 7:15)
5. c) earthquakes (Matthew 24:7)
6. "If ye abide in me, and my words abide in you . . ." (John 15:7)
7. a) faith (Romans 1:17)
8. d) Mount Sinai (Galatians 4:24-25)
9. poisonous (James 3:8)
10. a) loveth (1 John 4:8)

Teachings III

1. "a proud look," "a lying tongue," "hands that shed innocent blood," "an heart that deviseth wicked imaginations," "feet that be swift in running to mischief," "a false witness that speaketh lies," and "he that soweth discord among brethren" (Proverbs 6:16-19)
2. c) robbing Him (Malachi 3:8-12)
3. b) that He existed before Abraham (John 8:58-59)
4. d) Jesus (Matthew 6:9-13, Luke 11:2-4)
5. c) that there will be no marriages in heaven (Matthew 22:29-30)
6. d) the end of the world (Revelation 22:13)
7. b) Peter (Acts 2:1-21)
8. c) bodies (Romans 12:1)
9. two (1 and 2 Corinthians)
10. lose it for His sake (Matthew 16:25)

Tongues to Speak

1. True (Genesis 11:1)
2. a) sweet (Job 20:12)
3. d) entering God's holy tabernacle (Psalm 15:1-3)
4. b) "apples of gold in pictures of silver" (Proverbs 25:11)
5. c) Psalms (Psalm 34:13)
6. d) they will rot in their mouths (Zechariah 14:12)
7. a) two (John 8:17)
8. b) the Corinthians (1 Corinthians 14:1-14)
9. c) deadly poison (James 3:8)
10. False (Revelation 7:9-10)

Town and Country I

1. b) Jacob wrestled with God (Genesis 32:24-30)
2. c) Midian (Exodus 3:1)
3. a) Ramah (1 Samuel 8:4-5)
4. d) Gath (1 Samuel 17:4)
5. b) Ramah (1 Samuel 25:1, 28:3)
6. c) shadowing with wings (Isaiah 18:1)
7. d) Babylon (Daniel 6:16-23)
8. b) Bethlehem (Luke 2:4)
9. b) Nazareth (Luke 4:16-30)
10. b) to Emmaus (Luke 24:13)

Town and Country II

1. a) Enoch (Genesis 4:17)
2. a) Bethel (Genesis 35:8)
3. c) it's where Abraham, Isaac, Jacob, and their wives were buried (Genesis 49:28-33)
4. d) Shiloh (1 Samuel 1:24-28)
5. d) Capernaum (Matthew 4:12-13)
6. b) Jericho (Mark 10:46)
7. c) Bethany (John 11:1)
8. b) Jerusalem (Acts 2:1-13)
9. d) one of the seven churches with which God communicated in Revelation (Revelation 1:11, 3:7-13)
10. c) Patmos (Revelation 1:9)

Town and Country III

1. b) Ur (Genesis 11:31)
2. d) Salem (Genesis 14:18)
3. Pithom and Raamses (Exodus 1:11)
4. c) Ai (Joshua 8:1-29)
5. c) Bethlehem (Ruth 1:22-2:1)
6. b) Tyre (1 Kings 9:10-14)
7. b) Jerusalem (Zechariah 2:1-5)
8. d) Bethsaida (John 1:44)
9. b) Cyprus (Acts 13:4-5)
10. b) Thessalonica (Acts 20:4)

Trees and Flowers I

1. False (Genesis 1-2)
2. d) the trees of life and knowledge (Genesis 2:9)
3. cypress (Genesis 6:14)
4. shittim or acacia (Exodus 25:10)
5. c) bulrushes (Exodus 1:22-2:3)
6. c) tree (Exodus 15:23-25)
7. b) palm (Judges 4:5)
8. b) Lebanon (1 Kings 5:6-9)
9. b) willow (Psalms 137:2)
10. d) lilies (Matthew 6:28-29)

Trees and Flowers II

1. d) not known (Genesis 2:16-3:17)
2. d) the person who delights in God's law (Psalm 1:3)
3. c) the person who trusts in the Lord (Jeremiah 17:7-8)
4. sycamore (Luke 19:4)
5. b) Bashan (Zechariah 11:2)
6. c) fig (John 1:47-48)
7. b) mint, anise, cumin (Matthew 23:23)
8. a) cornfield (Matthew 12:1-2)
9. c) olive (Romans 11:17)
10. d) healing (Revelation 22:2)

Vital Statistics

1. c) forty (Genesis 7:12)
2. three (Genesis 6:16)
3. d) 142,000 (1 Kings 8:63)
4. a) the number of verses in each chapter is divisible by eleven
5. Jeremiah
6. 3 John—take credit also if you chose 2 John, which has one fewer verse
7. Esther 8:9
8. John 11:35—"Jesus wept."
9. a) five, two, one (Matthew 25:15)
10. d) 3,000 proverbs, 1,005 songs (1 Kings 4:32)

Waterways

1. c) all of it (Genesis 1:1-10)
2. d) rocks (Exodus 17:6)
3. c) Kidron (2 Samuel 15:23)
4. b) the River Jordan (2 Kings 2:6-11)
5. d) Hezekiah (2 Kings 20:20)
6. c) Heshbon (Song of Solomon 7:4)
7. b) Assyria (Isaiah 8:7-8)
8. a) River Jordan (Matthew 3:6)
9. b) the Pharisees (Luke 16:14-31)
10. c) Euphrates (Revelation 16:12)

Wayward Paths

1. d) Shinar (Genesis 11:1-4)
2. b) Edomites (Genesis 36:9)
3. c) ground the idol into powder, put it in water and made them drink it (Exodus 32:20)
4. a) were committed directly against God (1 Samuel 2:12-17, 2:22-36)
5. Er (1 Chronicles 2:3)
6. b) an ox bound for slaughter (Proverbs 7:22)
7. a) Noah and Lot (Luke 17:26-30)
8. d) Demas (2 Timothy 4:10)
9. c) Peter (2 Peter 3:3-4)
10. b) it recovers from a seemingly fatal wound (Revelation 13:3)

A Way with Words

1. c) Napthali (Genesis 49:21)
2. b) Jeremiah (Jeremiah 23:29)
3. His parents finding him in the temple at age twelve (Luke 2:49)
4. d) the Bible doesn't report what He wrote (John 8:1-11)
5. d) Hebrew, Greek, and Latin (John 19:19-20)
6. c) a den of thieves (Matthew 21:13)
7. b) branches (John 15:5)
8. b) not clarified in Scripture (no scriptural evidence beyond 2 Corinthians 12:7-10)
9. d) "sharper than any two-edged sword" (Hebrews 4:12)
10. c) prophesy about Christ's return (2 Thessalonians 2:2-3)

What's in a Name? I

1. a) Father of a Great Multitude (Genesis 17:5)
2. d) God was would add to her another son (Genesis 30:24)
3. b) fought Him (Genesis 32:24-28)
4. a) stranger (Exodus 2:22, 18:3)
5. c) Moses (Exodus 3:13-14)
6. c) Ecclesiastes (Ecclesiastes 1:1)
7. Solomon (Ecclesiastes 1:1)
8. a) John (Luke 1:63-64)
9. c) rock (John 1:42)
10. Golgotha, where Jesus died on the cross (Matthew 27:33)

What's in a Name? II

1. c) mother of all living (Genesis 3:20)
2. True (Hebrews 6:19)
3. False (no reference)
4. True (Psalm 18:2)
5. d) Napthali (Genesis 30:7-8)
6. d) Pharaoh's daughter (Exodus 2:10)
7. d) teacher (John 1:38)
8. c) because many spirits possessed him (Mark 5:1-17)
9. b) Joses (Acts 4:36)
10. d) Mercury/Jupiter (Acts 14:8-18)

What's in a Name? III

1. False—God let Adam name the animals (Genesis 2:19)
2. a) Ishmael (Genesis 16:11)
3. b) Benoni (Genesis 35:18)
4. c) dreamer (Genesis 37:19)
5. b) Zacharias (Luke 1:58-60)
6. b) bitter lot in life (Ruth 1:19-20)
7. c) Jedidiah (2 Samuel 12:24-25)
8. d) Daniel (Daniel 7:9)
9. c) Paul (2 Thessalonians 2:3)
10. a) Lion (Revelation 5:5)

Who Said That? I

1. c) King Cyrus (Ezra 1:2)
2. a) Joel and Amos (Joel 3:16, Amos 1:2)
3. c) an angel (Luke 2:10)
4. c) Amos (Amos 4:6)
5. d) John the Baptist (Matthew 3:1-3)
6. d) none of the above (Martin Luther said it.)
7. a) Jesus (Matthew 5:18)
8. b) Jesus (John 20:15)
9. d) James (James 2:26)
10. d) John (1 John 4:19)

Who Said That? II

1. a) God (Genesis 3:19)
2. a) Cain (Genesis 4:9)
3. d) Ruth (Ruth 1:16)
4. c) Isaiah (Isaiah 52:7)
5. b) Paul (Galatians 2:20)
6. c) Jesus (Luke 16:22)
7. d) Jesus (Matthew 6:24)
8. a) Peter (Matthew 16:23)
9. b) Isaiah (Isaiah 40:31)
10. d) Paul (1 Timothy 6:7)

Who Said That? III

1. d) Satan (Genesis 3:4)
2. c) John (Revelation 6:17)
3. c) John the Baptist (John 1:29)
4. b) Nicodemus (John 3:1-3)
5. b) Nicodemus (John 3:1-16)
6. d) Jesus (Matthew 9:37)
7. d) Paul (1 Corinthians 16:20)
8. d) Satan to Christ (Matthew 4:9)
9. b) Peter (Acts 3:6)
10. c) Judas (Matthew 27:4)

Who Said That? IV

1. b) Job (Job 3:2-3)
2. d) the author of Proverbs (Proverbs 6:9)
3. b) Abram (Genesis 12:1-3)
4. Joseph and Mary, His earthly parents (Luke 2:42-49)
5. d) Nathanael (John 1:46)
6. a) Zacchaeus (Luke 19:10)
7. d) Paul (1 Timothy 6:10)
8. d) Paul (2 Timothy 4:7)
9. d) Peter (2 Peter 3:8)
10. c) John (I John 5:4)

Who Said That? V

1. d) Jesus (Matthew 24:7, Mark 13:8, Luke 21:10)
2. c) Joshua (Joshua 24:15)
3. b) God to Samuel (1 Samuel 8:7)
4. c) Job (Job 1:21)
5. d) Andrew (John 1:41)
6. c) the father of a child Jesus exorcised (Mark 9:24)
7. c) Jesus' disciples (Matthew 19:25)
8. d) Thomas (John 20:29)
9. c) Peter (Acts 10:34-35)
10. c) their jailer (Acts 16:30)

Who Said That? VI

1. c) the author of Ecclesiastes (Ecclesiastes 12:12)
2. b) Isaiah (Isaiah 11:6)
3. d) Paul (Ephesians 4:26)
4. b) the mother of Samson (Judges 13:5)
5. c) Pontius Pilate (John 18:38)
6. d) the church at Laodicea (Revelation 3:14-15)
7. d) Peter (John 21:17-18)
8. d) God (Acts 9:4)
9. b) the Philippians (Philippians 4:13)
10. a) James (James 2:19)

Who Said That? VII

1. b) John (John 1:1)
2. d) Paul (2 Corinthians 9:7)
3. d) Joel (Joel 2:28)
4. a) Job (Job 19:25)
5. d) Paul (2 Corinthians 6:14)
6. c) Elisabeth (Luke 1:41-42)
7. d) Paul (1 Corinthians 7:9)
8. c) Paul (1 Corinthians 10:13)
9. c) James (James 4:8)
10. d) Jesus (John 8:45)

Who Said That? VIII

1. a) Jacob (Genesis 28:16)
2. c) Moses (Exodus 4:10)
3. d) Joshua (Joshua 7:25)
4. a) Nehemiah (Nehemiah 8:10)
5. b) Solomon (Proverbs 14:12)
6. a) a psalmist (Psalm 127:1)
7. c) Festus (Acts 26:24)
8. d) Paul (1 Corinthians 13:11)
9. c) Jesus (Matthew 12:30)
10. b) Pontius Pilate (John 18:36)

Who Was I? I

1. d) Samson's (Judges 16:4)
2. b) Naomi's daughter-in-law (Ruth 1:3-4)
3. b) Jeremiah's (Jeremiah 36:4, 45:1)
4. b) temple musicians (1 Chronicles 6:31-44)
5. a) King David's wife (1 Samuel 25:43)
6. c) Saul (2 Samuel 3:7)
7. d) Joab (2 Samuel 19:13-20:13)
8. c) Ahasuerus (Esther 1:19)
9. a) the high priest's servant whose ear was cut off as Jesus was being arrested (John 18:10)
10. c) helped carry Jesus' cross (Matthew 27:32)

Who Was I? II

1. a) Joseph's master in Egypt (Genesis 39:1)
2. c) Moses and Aaron (Exodus 6:20)
3. a) false goddess the Israelites worshipped (Judges 2:13, 10:6, etc.)
4. c) the wife of Hosea (Hosea 1:3)
5. d) took spices to Jesus' tomb (Mark 16:1)
6. a) Baruch and Jeremiah (Jeremiah 36:26)
7. b) a servant in the home of Mary the mother of John Mark (Acts 12:13)
8. c) first-century Christian teacher and preacher (Acts 18:24-28)
9. b) synagogue leader (Acts 18:12-17)
10. d) a companion of Paul (Acts 19:29, 20:4, 27:2; Colossians 4:10, etc.)

Who Was I? III

1. b) I emerged from the womb with a red string tied to my hand (Genesis 38:27-30)
2. b) Aaron (Numbers 20:28)
3. d) Philistines (Judges 16:23, 1 Samuel 5:2-5)
4. c) benefactors (2 Samuel 19:32)
5. b) Solomon (2 Samuel 12:24-25)
6. b) two of God's chosen craftsmen (Exodus 31:1-6)
7. c) disciples (Luke 24:18)
8. c) Paul (Acts 27:1-3)
9. d) Judas' successor with the apostles (Acts 1:23-26)
10. b) Felix (Acts 24:24)

Who Was I? IV

1. a) Joseph (Genesis 41:45)
2. d) stopped a plague (Numbers 25:6-8)
3. c) was married to Elkanah, Samuel's father (1 Samuel 1:1-2)
4. a) King David (2 Samuel 2-4)
5. b) Ephraim (1 Chronicles 7:20-24)
6. a) Ethiopia (Acts 8:27)
7. b) prophetess (2 Kings 22:14-20, 2 Chronicles 34:22-28)
8. c) scribe (Romans 16:22)
9. c) sheltering Paul and Silas (Acts 17:1-9)
10. c) Joel (Joel 1:1)

Who Was I? V

1. a) a heroic warrior (2 Samuel 23:33)
2. d) Rebekah's nurse (Genesis 35:8)
3. b) Moses (2 Timothy 3:8)
4. a) Noah (Genesis 10:1-2, Ezekiel 38-39, Revelation 20:8)
5. d) went to war against Sodom and Gomorrah (Genesis 14:1-2)
6. d) Rome (Romans 16:15)
7. d) Assyria (2 Kings 17:1-6)
8. b) burn Jerusalem (2 Kings 25:8-21)
9. d) Saul/Paul (Acts 21:40-22:3)
10. c) silversmith who made idols (Acts 19:24)

Bonus Bible Hodgepodge

1. False (e.g,. Genesis 1:1)
2. b) crop farmer (Genesis 4:2)
3. c) Jared (Genesis 5:20, 5:27)
4. d) one pair of unclean animals, seven pairs of clean animals and birds (Genesis 7:2-3)
5. b) insufficient grazing land for their livestock (Genesis 13:5-7)
6. c) archer (Genesis 21:20)
7. a) in a cave (Genesis 25:9)
8. d) that his sons bury him in Canaan (Genesis 49:29-30)
9. c) like thorns in the Israelites' sides (Numbers 33:55)
10. d) no excuse (Jonah 1)
11. unleavened (Exodus 12:15)
12. True (Exodus 22:25)
13. d) as the place for the Israelites to confer with God (Exodus 33:7)
14. True (Leviticus 19:28)
15. c) it was placed in the Ark of the Covenant (Hebrews 9:3-4)
16. d) Og (Deuteronomy 3:11)
17. False—he bet clothing (Judges 14:10-18)
18. b) looking for his father's donkeys (1 Samuel 9:1-3)
19. b) Jonathan (1 Samuel 18:1)
20. b) Absalom (2 Samuel 14:25-26)
21. c) heads of families and King Cyrus (Ezra 2:69, 6:4)
22. Eliphaz, Bildad, and Zophar (Job 2:11)
23. Malachi
24. c) 969 (Genesis 5:27)
25. b) brothers (Exodus 4:14)
26. c) feeding 5,000 with loaves and fishes (Matthew 14, Mark 6, Luke 9, John 6)
27. a) from Jerusalem to Jericho (Luke 10:30)
28. d) Father (Mark 14:36, Romans 8:15, Galatians 4:6)
29. a) washing their hands before eating (Matthew 15:1-2, Mark 7:5)
30. True
31. c) Caesar's (Matthew 22:19-22)
32. c) 70 years (Psalm 90:10)
33. a) the way of a lion on the prowl (Proverbs 30:18-19)
34. c) whip (John 2:14-15)
35. d) money changing in the Jerusalem temple (John 2:13-17)
36. d) Simon (Luke 7:36-50)
37. Father, Son, Holy Spirit (Matthew 28:19, 2 Corinthians 13:14)
38. c) prayer and drawing lots (Acts 1:23-26)
39. d) life (Revelation 20:12)
40. Amen (Revelation 22:21)